# THE EVOLUTION
# OF THE HUMAN
# BRAIN

# THE SCIENTIST'S LIBRARY
*Biology and Medicine*

EDITED BY
PETER P. H. De BRUYN, M.D.

# THE EVOLUTION OF THE HUMAN BRAIN

BY

GERHARDT VON BONIN

*Professor of Anatomy Emeritus, University of Illinois*
*Consultant in Neuroanatomy, Mount Zion Hospital*
*San Francisco*

THE UNIVERSITY OF CHICAGO PRESS

# THE UNIVERSITY OF CHICAGO COMMITTEE ON PUBLICATIONS IN BIOLOGY AND MEDICINE

EMMET B. BAY · LOWELL T. COGGESHALL
LESTER R. DRAGSTEDT · FRANKLIN C. McLEAN
THOMAS PARK · WILLIAM H. TALIAFERRO

*Library of Congress Catalog Card Number: 63-13062*

THE UNIVERSITY OF CHICAGO PRESS, CHICAGO & LONDON

Midway Reprint    1974

# Preface to the Series

During the past few decades the investigative approaches to biological problems have become markedly diversified. This diversification has been caused in part by the introduction of methods from other fields, such as mathematics, physics, and chemistry, and in part has been brought about by the formulation of new problems within biology. At the same time, the quantity of scientific production and publication has increased. Under these circumstances, the biologist has to focus his attention more and more exclusively on his own field of interest. This specialization, effective as it is in the pursuit of individual problems, requiring ability and knowledge didactically unrelated to biology, is detrimental to a broad understanding of the current aspects of biology as a whole, without which conceptual progress is difficult.

The purpose of "The Scientist's Library: Biology and Medicine" series is to provide authoritative information about the growth and status of various subjects in such a fashion that the individual books may be read with profit not only by the specialist but also by those whose interests lie in other fields. The topics for the series have been selected as representative of active fields of science, especially those that have developed markedly in recent years as the result of new methods and new discoveries. The textual approach is somewhat different from that ordinarily used by the specialist. The authors have been asked to emphasize introductory concepts and problems, and the present status of their subjects, and to clarify terminology and methods of approach instead of limiting themselves to detailed accounts of current factual knowledge. The authors have also been asked to assume a common level of scientific competence rather than to attempt popularization of the subject matter.

Consequently, the books should be of interest and value to workers in the various fields of biology and medicine. For the teacher and investigator, and for students entering specialized areas, they will provide familiarity with the aims, achievements, and present status of these fields.

PETER P. H. DE BRUYN

CHICAGO, ILLINOIS

# Foreword

To write a new book these days, one must have good reasons, since the market is already flooded with far too many books. For producing the present, fortunately slender, volume, the writer offers two: first, this volume is a report of the Wenner-Gren, National Science, and Guggenheim foundations, with whose financial help the material on which this book is based was gathered; and, second, the writer can claim to be one of the few people who have worked in both anthropology and neurology and therefore may be able to tackle the problems here discussed with some degree of confidence.

This book treats of the evolution of the human brain from Australopithecus to modern man. It does not try to go further back in time, for that has been done very ably by others. It is a peculiarity of this book that it has a largely negative aspect, as it demolishes exaggerated claims about what can be learned from fossil endocasts. To do that without making everybody angry who has in the course of time advanced such claims is not easy. I hope to have avoided, on the whole, treading too heavily on anybody's toes, and I would like to take this opportunity to assure the reader that my intention was certainly not to offend anyone.

The few things I did discover about the brain of fossil man need corroboration, naturally, since no good scientist should ever take one opinion as the gospel truth. But even if the place of Neanderthal man should change, it is hoped that the general tenor of this book may survive any detailed criticism that can be leveled against it.

At this time, too, I wish to acknowledge the help I received in the preparation of this manuscript from both the Department of Anatomy of the University of California and the Neurosurgical Department of Mount Zion Hospital in San Francisco. My thanks also go to the above-mentioned foundations.

G. v. B.

SAN FRANCISCO
*September 1962*

# Contents

# *Figures*

# *Tables*

## Tables

# CHAPTER I

# Man and the Anthropoids

By way of introduction and to lay a basis for a better appreciation of the role of the cortex in the human brain, we will first touch on a few points in the evolution of the brain prior to the primate stage.

The brain of primitive vertebrates, such as fish or even Amphibia, has no cortex in the sense in which this word is used for mammals. It has only a thin layer a few cells thick on the surface of the cerebral hemisphere, which does not seem to have the functions of the mammalian cortex. It appears to receive olfactory impulses almost exclusively. The brain of these lowly forms is, in other words, essentially brain stem, and it is, of course, of some interest to find out how these forms move or perceive. Not too much is known about these functions, although it is an obvious conclusion to locate them in the reticular substance of the brain stem, since, as we have just hinted, the forebrain is essentially no more than an olfactory center. That the reticular substance in fish is different from that in mammals seems certain; Beccari (1922, 1930) has shown that in fish the reticular substance consists mainly of condensations of cells in the vicinity of the nuclei of the cranial nerves and that it is histologically not highly differentiated. In mammals, on the other hand, it occupies large parts of the brain stem and can be grouped into numerous nuclei of very different appearance (Brodal, 1957). That the spinal cord in fish must be rather differently organized from the spinal cord of mammals is equally clear, but little precise knowledge is available. Fish appear to have no long ascending or descending tracts, and it is very doubtful that there is a two-neuron reflex arc in fish as we find in mammals.

1

From a paper by Kruger and Berkowitz (1960) it appears that even such reptiles as the alligator do not have a cortex in the mammalian sense, although there is a projection of somatic and visual impulses on the cortical surface. The fields for the various afferent systems are not laid out separately as in mammals, and there seem to be no thalamic projections. The authors apparently feel that alligators and mammals cannot be directly compared and that the alligator probably represents another line of evolution and is not in the direct line of mammalian ascent. We would agree with them.

Among mammals a cortex which can properly be so called certainly develops in the Eutheria. The case for the monotremes and the marsupials is not quite so clear, and further work is required. The evolution of the cortex leads to tremendous changes in practically all parts of the brain. The thalamus becomes, in its dorsal part, almost completely dependent on the cortex, in the sense that it receives fibers carrying sensory messages, filters them or works them over in a way which is only imperfectly understood, and sends them on to the cortex, where they arrive in separate fields, clearly laid apart from each other.

There is also an enormous change in the structure of the reticular substance of the brain stem, which stands from the very beginning of the evolutionary process in a two-way connection with the cortex. A number of different structures develop in the brain stem and in the cerebellum which are dependent on the cortex and which are frequently classed together under the name of extrapyramidal system. It is not our purpose here to go into any details about these structures; all we want to do now is to point out that the mammalian brain differs very considerably in almost all its parts from that of the lower vertebrates.

Turning for a moment to the sensory system, we should bear in mind that the cortex and the reticular system evidently work on quite different lines. In the cortex, the sensory impulses are neatly laid apart according to a topographical principle, so that for each impulse a certain place in the cortex is reserved, so to speak, whereas in the reticular substance, the convergence of many (and frequently variegated) impulses on the same group of cells

2

(if not on the same cell) appears to be the guiding principle of its organization. What this difference means in terms of function, we do not know yet, but we should certainly keep in mind that a synthesis of the various sensory modalities can be achieved much more easily in the reticular substance than in the cortex (Scheibel and Scheibel, 1958).

One of the most important differences between higher and lower vertebrates that we are just beginning to appreciate is the much less variegated sensory input of the lower forms and the importance of this fact for the intelligence of the animal. In this connection it should be particularly pointed out that one of the most important differences between primates and other mammals is that the former rely more on vision than olfaction and, consequently, that the optic nerve gets much bigger and contains many more fibers than in other forms. To cite but a few examples: dog and cat, about 150,000 fibers; pig and sheep, about 600,000; and monkey and man, about 1,200,000. This means, of course, that there is a much richer sensory input in primates than in other forms. Since it has been shown (D. O. Hebb, 1949; and others) that the sensory input is necessary for a normal life of the cortex —at least in man—this may partly explain the greater intelligence of the primates, although it certainly is not the only factor.

So much by way of a general introduction. What we want to study here are the final steps in the evolution of the human brain. It is customary to start with the great apes, then go on to the fossil forms, and end up with modern man. It is often not sufficiently realized that in proceeding thus we mix two lines of thought which should be kept separate; for the great apes—we can lump them all together for the moment—are after all contemporaneous forms. The fossil forms through which man went, however, probably looked different from, although similar to, them. A short consideration of the anatomy of the great apes will make it quite clear where they stand in the evolutionary scale and how far we can make use of them for our present theme.

We shall start with the number of vertebrae, for which Schultz (1945) has given us good material. The original number of vertebrae seems to have been 7 cervical, 13 thoracic, and 6 lumbar.

The number has gradually become reduced with the result that we frequently find a lesser number in higher forms. Seven cervical vertebrae are present in practically all mammals, with one or two exceptions, but the numbers of thoracic and lumbar vertebrae vary much more, as Tables 1 and 2 show. The reduction of the

### TABLE 1
#### NUMBER OF THORACIC VERTEBRAE IN PRIMATES*

| PRIMATE | NUMBER OF CASES | NUMBER OF VERTEBRAE | | | | | | | | AVERAGE NUMBER OF VERTEBRAE |
|---|---|---|---|---|---|---|---|---|---|---|
| | | 11 | 11½ | 12 | 12½ | 13 | 13½ | 14 | 15 | |
| | | Frequency of Occurrence (in Per Cent) | | | | | | | | |
| Cebus | 37 | | | 5.4 | | 13.5 | | 70.3 | 10.8 | 13.9 |
| Ateles | 20 | | | | | 10.0 | | 90.0 | | 13.9 |
| Alouatta | 24 | | | | | 16.7 | | 70.8 | 12.5 | 14.0 |
| Hylobates | 57 | | | 15.8 | | 75.4 | | 8.8 | | 12.9 |
| Symphalangus | 16 | | | 12.5 | | 87.6 | | | | 12.9 |
| Pithecus | 50 | | | 92.0 | | 8.0 | | | | 12.1 |
| Pan | 55 | | | 12.7 | 1.8 | 74.6 | 1.8 | 9.1 | | 13.0 |
| Gorilla gorilla | 75 | | | 5.3 | | 86.7 | | 8.0 | | 13.0 |
| Gorilla beringei | 7 | | | 42.9 | | 57.1 | | | | 12.6 |
| Pongo | 79 | 12.7 | 6.3 | 72.1 | 1.3 | 7.6 | | | | 11.9 |
| Negro | 161 | 5.0 | | 91.3 | | 3.7 | | | | 12.0 |
| Japanese | 429 | 0.2 | 0.5 | 96.0 | 0.7 | 2.6 | | | | 12.0 |
| White | 766 | 2.1 | 0.1 | 94.0 | 0.1 | 3.7 | | | | 12.0 |

* After Schultz, 1945.

number of thoracic vertebrae has gone furthest in the human stock, with one exception—Pongo—whereas the number of lumbar vertebrae has been reduced further in the great apes than in man. It is also of some interest to consider a rank based on a combination of the numbers of thoracic and lumbar vertebrae, since this arranges the animals in a slightly different order, as shown in Table 3. Considering merely the number of thoracic vertebrae, we get the order (from highest to lowest): Pan, Gorilla, Hylobates, Man, and Pongo; taking the lumbar vertebrae as our guide, we get (from lowest to highest): Gorilla, Pan, Pongo, Hylobates, and Man; and taking the sum of both, we obtain (from highest to lowest); Hylobates, Man, Pan, Gorilla, and Pongo. Counting the number of sacral vertebrae (Table 4), we get the order (from lowest to highest): Hylobates, Pongo, Man, Pan, and Gorilla. Although all the orders are different, it is clear at any rate that

TABLE 2

NUMBER OF LUMBAR VERTEBRAE IN PRIMATES*

| PRIMATE | NUMBER OF CASES | NUMBER OF VERTEBRAE | | | | | | | AVERAGE NUMBER OF VERTEBRAE |
| | | 3 | 3½ | 4 | 4½ | 5 | 6 | 7 | |
| | | Frequency of Occurrence (in Per Cent) | | | | | | | |
| Cebus............ | 37 | .... | .... | 2.7 | .... | 35.5 | 56.2 | 5.4 | 5.6 |
| Ateles............ | 20 | .... | .... | 100.0 | .... | .... | .... | .... | 4.0 |
| Alouatta......... | 24 | .... | .... | .... | .... | 91.7 | 8.3 | .... | 5.1 |
| Hylobates........ | 57 | .... | .... | 8.4 | .... | 86.2 | 5.4 | .... | 5.0 |
| Symphalangus.... | 16 | .... | .... | 37.5 | .... | 56.2 | 6.3 | .... | 4.7 |
| Pithecus.......... | 50 | .... | .... | .... | .... | .... | 16.0 | 84.0 | 6.8 |
| Pan.............. | 55 | 16.4 | 3.6 | 74.5 | .... | 5.5 | .... | .... | 3.9 |
| Gorilla gorilla..... | 75 | 38.7 | .... | 60.0 | .... | 1.3 | .... | .... | 3.6 |
| Gorilla beringei... | 7 | 57.1 | .... | 42.9 | .... | .... | .... | .... | 3.4 |
| Pongo............ | 79 | 5.1 | 5.1 | 78.5 | 2.5 | 8.8 | .... | .... | 4.0 |
| Negro............ | 160 | .... | .... | 7.5 | .... | 86.3 | 6.2 | .... | 5.0 |
| Japanese......... | 148 | .... | .... | 2.7 | .... | 91.2 | 6.1 | .... | 5.0 |
| White............ | 766 | .... | .... | 2.3 | 0.1 | 93.3 | 4.3 | .... | 5.0 |

* After Schultz, 1945.

man cannot be considered the most progressive animal, for in only one instance is man at the end of the line, so to speak. Since the number of vertebrae is fairly well fixed genetically, we can assume that man and the great apes parted ways fairly early in phylogenesis. Although the lumbar region will be a little less movable when it is composed of four instead of five vertebrae, the difference in movability cannot be very great. In any event, it occurs every now and then in man with no visible disturbance in the motility of the trunk.

Taking a glance at the coccygeal vertebrae, we see that they

5

are rudimentary in all forms, since none of the great apes has a visible tail. From Table 5 we note that, on the average, man has kept more of a tail than the great apes. The reduction has gone further in all other forms, furthest in the brachiator Hylobates. It is doubtful that there is any correlation with the reduction in

### TABLE 3

NUMBER OF THORACO-LUMBAR VERTEBRAE IN PRIMATES*

| PRIMATE | NUM- BER OF CASES | NUMBER OF VERTEBRAE | | | | | | | AVERAGE NUMBER OF VERTEBRAE |
|---|---|---|---|---|---|---|---|---|---|
| | | 15 | 16 | 17 | 18 | 19 | 20 | 21 | |
| | | Frequency of Occurrence (in Per Cent) | | | | | | | |
| Cebus........... | 38 | .... | .... | .... | 3.6 | 44.4 | 48.4 | 3.6 | 19.5 |
| Ateles.......... | 22 | .... | .... | 13.6 | 86.4 | .... | .... | | 17.9 |
| Alouatta........ | 25 | .... | .... | .... | 12.0 | 68.0 | 20.0 | .... | 19.1 |
| Hylobates....... | 63 | .... | .... | 17.5 | 76.2 | 6.3 | .... | | 17.9 |
| Symphalangus... | 18 | .... | .... | 44.4 | 55.6 | .... | .... | | 17.6 |
| Pithecus......... | 53 | .... | .... | .... | 7.5 | 92.5 | .... | | 18.9 |
| Pan............. | 63 | 1.6 | 19.0 | 74.6 | 4.8 | .... | .... | | 16.8 |
| Gorilla gorilla.... | 75 | 1.3 | 34.2 | 63.2 | 1.3 | .... | .... | | 16.6 |
| Gorilla beringei.. | 7 | .... | 100.0 | .... | .... | .... | .... | | 16.0 |
| Pongo........... | 79 | 14.5 | 75.9 | 9.6 | .... | .... | .... | | 16.0 |
| Negro........... | 347 | .... | 4.0 | 90.5 | 5.5 | .... | .... | | 17.0 |
| Japanese........ | 329 | .... | 2.7 | 90.6 | 6.7 | .... | .... | | 17.0 |
| White........... | 3,180 | .... | 2.8 | 92.3 | 4.9 | .... | .... | | 17.0 |

* After Schultz, 1945.

numbers of the lumbar vertebrae, particularly since in the order based on those numbers the Hylobates stands in quite a different place.

The work of Slijper (1946), which is much too long to be reviewed adequately in this context, contains some points that are pertinent here. The inclination and the size of the neural spines in man are different from those of the anthropoid apes (Fig. 1). This is obviously largely a matter of functional adaptation, since man is the only form that habitually walks upright. Man is further removed from the original primate configuration

## TABLE 4

### NUMBER OF SACRAL VERTEBRAE IN PRIMATES*

| PRIMATE | NUMBER OF CASES | NUMBER OF VERTEBRAE | | | | | | AVERAGE NUMBER OF VERTEBRAE |
|---|---|---|---|---|---|---|---|---|
| | | 2 | 3 | 4 | 5 | 6 | 7 | |
| | | Frequency of Occurrence (in Per Cent) | | | | | | |
| Cebus............ | 37 | 2.7 | 97.3 | ..... | ..... | ..... | ..... | 3.0 |
| Ateles............ | 20 | ..... | 95.0 | 5.0 | ..... | ..... | ..... | 3.1 |
| Alouatta......... | 24 | ..... | 91.7 | 8.3 | ..... | ..... | ..... | 3.1 |
| Hylobates........ | 54 | ..... | ..... | 59.3 | 40.7 | ..... | ..... | 4.1 |
| Symphalangus.... | 16 | ..... | 6.2 | 56.4 | 31.2 | 6.2 | ..... | 4.4 |
| Pithecus......... | 50 | ..... | 100.0 | ..... | ..... | ..... | ..... | 3.0 |
| Pan............. | 42 | ..... | ..... | 4.8 | 47.6 | 47.6 | ..... | 5.4 |
| Gorilla gorilla.... | 54 | ..... | ..... | ..... | 50.0 | 48.2 | 1.8 | 5.5 |
| Gorilla beringei... | 7 | ..... | ..... | ..... | 28.6 | 71.4 | ..... | 5.7 |
| Pongo........... | 88 | ..... | ..... | 11.4 | 68.4 | 20.2 | ..... | 5.1 |
| Negro........... | 155 | ..... | ..... | ..... | 89.0 | 11.0 | ..... | 5.1 |
| Japanese......... | 181 | ..... | ..... | 1.1 | 70.2 | 28.7 | ..... | 5.3 |
| White........... | 631 | ..... | ..... | 1.0 | 76.9 | 21.9 | 0.2 | 5.2 |

* After Schultz, 1945,

## TABLE 5

### NUMBER OF COCCYGEAL VERTEBRAE IN PRIMATES*

| PRIMATE | NUMBER OF CASES | NUMBER OF VERTEBRAE | | | | | | AVERAGE NUMBER OF VERTEBRAE |
|---|---|---|---|---|---|---|---|---|
| | | 1 | 2 | 3 | 4 | 5 | 6 | |
| | | Frequency of Occurrence (in Per Cent) | | | | | | |
| Homo........... | 745 | ..... | ..... | 11.9 | 61.1 | 27.0 | ..... | 4.2 |
| Pan............. | 28 | ..... | 25.0 | 35.7 | 28.6 | 7.1 | 3.6 | 3.3 |
| Gorilla gorilla.... | 29 | ..... | 24.1 | 44.9 | 24.1 | 6.9 | ..... | 3.1 |
| Gorilla beringei... | 4 | ..... | 25.0 | 50.0 | 25.0 | ..... | ..... | 3.0 |
| Pongo........... | 61 | 3.7 | 27.5 | 54.0 | 11.5 | 3.3 | ..... | 2.8 |
| Symphalangus.... | 9 | 11.1 | 22.2 | 44.6 | 22.2 | ..... | ..... | 2.8 |
| Hylobates........ | 46 | 10.9 | 37.0 | 32.6 | 15.2 | 4.3 | ..... | 2.6 |

* After Schultz, 1945.

than the anthropoid apes, confirming what has been seen in other instances.

We turn next to the sacrum, which, in primitive forms, appears to be composed of 3 vertebrae (Table 4). In man, the average number is a little higher than 5; in the Hylobates, it is 4.1 or 4.4; in the great apes other than Hylobates, it is about 5.5. But the main point is that this characteristic is much more stable in man than in the apes. This is clearly due to his upright posture. That

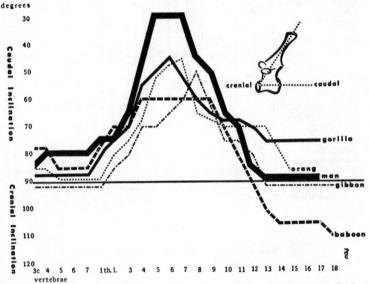

Fig. 1.—Inclination of the neural spines in some primates. (After Slijper, 1946.)

the sacrum shows a pronounced promontory only in man, and not in the apes or any lower forms, is well known and is depicted once more in Figure 2, which has been taken from Schultz (1949). What this means, in effect, is that only in man has the presacral part of the trunk, or rather the thoraco-lumbar part of the spine, acquired an upright position by the bending of the lower part of the lumbar region of the spine and not at all by the turning in of the acetabulum as occurred in the true brachiators.

What is most characteristic of the human pelvis is the broadness and the short length of the ilium. This comes out in Table 6,

## TABLE 6

### ILIUM LENGTH AND PROPORTIONS OF PELVIS (IN MM.)*

| Primate | Number of Cases | 1† | 2 | 3 | 4 | 5 | 6 | 7 |
|---|---|---|---|---|---|---|---|---|
| Cebus............... | 2 | 63 | 184 | 81 | 38 | 70 | 32 | 0.0 |
| Ateles............... | 1 | 100 | 227 | 102 | 42 | 95 | 152 | − 3.4 |
| Pithecus............ | 2 | 90 | 204 | 91 | 37 | 76 | 81 | +14.1 |
| Hylobates.......... | 23 | 87 | 231 | 95 | 51 | 118 | 224 | − 4.7 |
| Symphalangus....... | 4 | 109 | 252 | 112 | 62 | 156 | 278 | − 4.2 |
| Pongo.............. | 2 | 157 | 200 | 99 | 77 | 147 | 261 | − 7.0 |
| Pan................ | 2 | 173 | 199 | 82 | 62 | 124 | 305 | − 4.5 |
| Gorilla gorilla....... | 9 | 216 | 187 | 95 | 90 | 107 | 394 | −15.0 |
| Homo.............. | 15 | 127 | 139 | 89 | 122 | 169 | 152 | −13.4 |

\* After Schultz, 1949.
† 1: length of ilium
  2: ilium/ischium length
  3: pubis/ischium length
  4: ilium width/length
  5: ilium width/ischium length
  6: fossa iliaca width/sacral surface width
  7: fossa iliaca depth/width ( +: convex toward the inner side; −: concave toward the inner side)

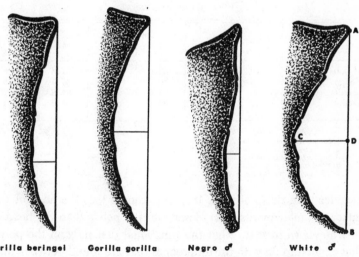

Gorilla beringei    Gorilla gorilla    Negro ♂    White ♂

FIG. 2.—Midsagittal sections through the sacra of gorilla and man. (After Schultz, 1949.) *A* is the promontory; *B* is the lowest end of the sacrum; *C* is the deepest part of the sacrum; and *CD* is the perpendicular from *C* on *AB*.

which gathers some indices to illustrate this and a few related points. The sexual differences in the pelvis are, naturally, also of great interest. We know something about the weight of the new-born in relation to that of its mother. The newborn are larger in man than they are in the great apes (Table 7), with the exception of the Hylobates, but the newborn of monkeys are generally

### TABLE 7

PER CENT OF WEIGHT OF NEWBORN IN
WEIGHT OF MOTHER

| Primate | Per Cent |
|---|---|
| Cebus | 8.5 |
| Macaque | 6.7 |
| Hylobates | 7.5 |
| Orangutan | 4.1 |
| Chimpanzee | 4.0 |
| Gorilla | 2.4 |
| Man | 5.5 |

### TABLE 8

FOOT MEASUREMENTS*

| Primate | Number of Cases | 1† | 2 | 3 | 4 | 5 |
|---|---|---|---|---|---|---|
| Hylobates | 10 | 28.2 | 30.6 | 41.2 | 67.3 | 83.2 |
| Pongo | 5 | 26.1 | 30.6 | 43.3 | 35.5 | 31.5 |
| Gorilla | 9 | 39.5 | 27.6 | 32.9 | 64.8 | 88.7 |
| Homo | 10 | 49.2 | 29.6 | 21.2 | 97.2 | 93.1 |

\* Condensed from Schultz, 1930.

† 1: tarsus/total length of foot
  2: metatarsus III/total length
  3: phalanges/total length of foot
  4: ray I/ray III (ray: metatarsus + phalanges)
  5: phalanges I/metatarsus I

heavier than those of man. It is also known that the head of the macaque monkey fits even closer into the pelvis than the head of the newborn in man. That the functional demands on the pelvis have much to do with the differences that are found between man and the great apes is obvious and puts the value of the pelvis as an indicator of the phylogenetic status on a much lower level than the presacral thoraco-lumbar vertebral column.

The foot has, of course, become highly specialized through the assumption of upright posture. A few indices of these changes are given in Tables 8 and 9. These tables show that, in relation to the whole foot, the tarsus is relatively much longer in man than in the great apes. They also show the reduction in the length of the third toe in relation to the first one. That in this case the second phalanx bore the brunt of the reduction becomes clear from Table 9. In this connection, we will examine for a moment the musculature of the foot of some primates (Fig. 3), as they have been depicted by Straus (1949). From these diagrams it appears to be easier to derive the condition in man from that of Prosimiae than from the condition either in Hylobates or in great apes, and the

TABLE 9

RELATION OF LENGTH OF THE PHALANGES OF MIDDLE TOE
TO TOTAL LENGTH OF ALL PHALANGES

| PRIMATE | NUMBER OF CASES | PHALANGES OF MIDDLE TOE (PER CENT) | | |
|---|---|---|---|---|
| | | Basal | Middle | Third |
| Hylobates.......... | 10 | 50.4 | 32.5 | 17.0 |
| Pongo............. | 5 | 53.1 | 32.2 | 14.6 |
| Gorilla............ | 9 | 49.1 | 31.0 | 19.9 |
| Homo............. | 10 | 52.8 | 23.9 | 23.3 |

presence of a well-developed quadratus plantae points in the same direction. All these things can, of course, be explained by the plantigrade locomotion on flat ground that is peculiar to man, but the fact remains that the pattern in man is closer to that of the lower apes than to that of the anthropoids.

A few words regarding the relations of the lengths of the long bones may not be amiss, although this characteristic is again obviously very greatly influenced by the way in which the animals move about. Table 10 gives the indices and the absolute values for the humerus. The crural index, defining the relation of the tibia and femur, does not differ very much among all of the primates. The brachial index, that is, the relation of humerus to ulna and radius, is lowest in man and, as was to be expected, highest in Hylobates; the intermembral index, defining the lengths of humerus and ulna in relation to femur and tibia, also varies consid-

11

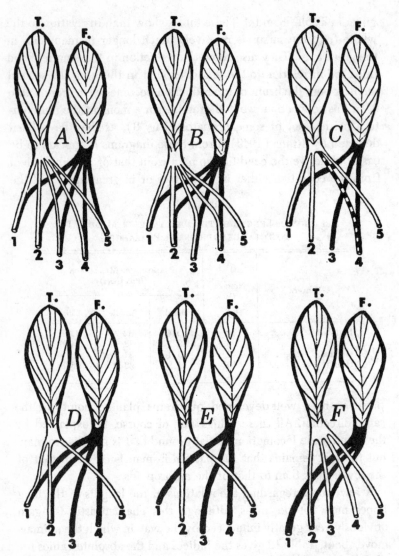

Fig. 3.—Diagrams to show the various types of distributions of the tendons of the long flexor muscles of the toes (flexor digitorum tibialis, *T.*; flexor digitorum fibularus, *F.*) in primates. (After Straus, 1949.) *A*, prosimians, typical; *B*, platyrrhine monkeys (Cebidae), typical; *C*, catarrhine monkeys (Cercopithecidae), typical; *D*, gibbons and sia-mangs (Hylobatidae), typical; *E*, great apes (Pongidae), typical (in the orangutan, the tendon to the great toe is regularly absent); *F*, man, typical.

erably from form to form and is again highest in Hylobates, who have, in other words, the longest arms.

From the pen of Miller (1947), we have an interesting study of the inguinal canal of the primates, in which the author makes the following statement: "A well developed inguinal ligament is only found in man. In the apes the aponeurosis of the abdominal muscles merely forms a series of arches over the structures that

TABLE 10

HUMERUS LENGTH AND LIMB PROPORTIONS IN PRIMATES*

| Primate | Number of Cases | 1† | 2 | 3 | 4 |
|---|---|---|---|---|---|
| Hylobates...... | 24 | 226.4 | 113.3 | 88.5 | 128.3 |
| Symphalangus.. | 13 | 269.2 | 111.3 | 86.3 | 148.2 |
| Pongo......... | 66 | 343.7 | 100.7 | 91.9 | 143.8 |
| Pan........... | 29 | 299.8 | 92.6 | 83.7 | 107.7 |
| Gorilla gorilla... | 51 | 404.3 | 80.7 | 80.3 | 117.0 |
| Ainu.......... | 49 | 289.4 | 76.9 | 86.6 | 71.8 |
| Negro......... | 11 | 303.6 | 75.6 | 86.3 | 69.9 |
| White......... | 11 | 305.7 | 75.3 | 84.3 | 70.9 |

* Condensed from Schultz, 1930.
† 1: humerus length, in mm.
  2: brachial index
  3: crural index
  4: intermembral index

pass underneath them. A reflected inguinal ligament is likewise found only in man, although there are indications of it in Chimpanzee and Gorilla." In man the inguinal canal is essentially straight and forms a large angle with the surface of the abdominal wall; in the other primates it is oblique and forms a small angle with the wall. Man depends largely upon the inguinal ligament and tendinous ansa for support; in all other primates this support is furnished by the muscles. The cremaster is much less developed in man. There is in this respect a greater difference between man and the great apes than between the latter and the lower primates.

Another interesting line of research concerns the dermatoglyphics of the hand and the foot. It is well known that both the vola manus and the planta pedis bear ridges on the skin that represent different patterns in different individuals. In embryos

13

one frequently sees pads on the vola and the planta, and it is on these pads that the ridges develop. The ridges may be whorls, S-shaped, loops, or arches, and they may degenerate until they become mere parallel lines or open fields. By arranging them in a sequence, one can get an impression of the pattern intensity of a field—where the whorl has the highest value, the loop has the next highest, and the arch is of the simplest type (see Table 11, which contains an abstract of tables from Midlo and Cummins [1942]). It appears that pads are well developed in animals that walk, but not in those that use the extremity for "manipulation," if that term may be used. We find that the lines are less compli-

TABLE 11

PATTERN INTENSITY IN PALMS
AND SOLES OF PRIMATES*

| Primate | Palm | Sole |
|---------|------|------|
| Hylobates............. | 1.40 | 0.98 |
| Pongo................ | 3.01 | 1.77 |
| Gorilla.............. | 2.94 | 2.57 |
| Pan.................. | 2.06 | 2.01 |
| Homo................. | 1.14 | 2.52 |

*After Midlo and Cummins, 1942. The types of patterns were given arbitrary numbers and were then arranged in a sequence.

cated on the palm of man than on the palm of the apes, but that the reverse holds true for the sole of the foot, on which man has a higher pattern intensity than most apes. It is consistent with other findings that the gorilla, who almost always remains on the ground, has a plantar pattern which, in its intensity, is very similar to that of man. We do not intend to follow Midlo and Cummins all the way in their phylogenetic considerations, tempting though it may be. Their study is not sufficiently close to our proper theme, which is, after all, the brain, and for which this chapter is merely intended to lay the groundwork.

We turn to the head as that part of the body which is closest to the brain. Again we do not want to go into a detailed comparison of the skulls of man and the great apes but merely want to bring out a few points which seem to be of interest in the present connection. First of all, it appears to be of importance to discover how well the skull can be balanced on the spine. For this purpose, we can measure the amount of skull that is in front of and behind the condyles. This has been done numerous times, and the figures by Mollison using the skulls of chimpanzee and man have been reproduced in many textbooks (for example, see Braus, 1960, p. 657, Fig. 316). Schultz (1955) has recently made a new type of

TABLE 12

POSITION OF OCCIPITAL CONDYLES AND OF FACE*

| Primate | Sex | Number of Cases | 1† | 2 |
|---|---|---|---|---|
| Hylobates............ | M | 7 | 87.2 | + 7.0 |
|  | F | 7 | 91.0 | + 6.4 |
| Symphalangus........ | M | 7 | 90.8 | +12.2 |
|  | F | 7 | 93.8 | +14.2 |
| Pongo............... | M | 6 | 91.8 | +17.7 |
|  | F | 10 | 95.3 | +28.2 |
| Gorilla.............. | M | 12 | 93.3 | − 1.6 |
|  | F | 15 | 93.9 | +11.2 |
| Pan................. | M | 15 | 88.3 | + 5.9 |
|  | F | 17 | 88.4 | + 6.7 |
| Plesianthropus........ | F | 1 | 74.6 | + 2.2 |
| Rhodesian Man...... | M | 1 | 65.1 | −17.2 |
| White.............. | M | 15 | 65.8 | −16.8 |
|  | F | 15 | 65.8 | −17.3 |
| Australian........... | M | 15 | 66.6 | −11.2 |
|  | F | 15 | 67.3 | −11.7 |
| Negro............... | M | 15 | 68.0 | −10.7 |
|  | F | 15 | 68.3 | −11.8 |
| North Chinese........ | M | 10 | 68.8 | −10.7 |
|  | F | 15 | 68.8 | −18.0 |
| Eskimo.............. | M | 15 | 68.6 | −14.9 |
|  | F | 15 | 68.4 | −16.3 |

* After Schultz, 1955.

† 1: n-co/n-op (nasion-condylion/nasion-opisthion)
2: n-pr/n-op (nasion-prosthion/nasion-opisthion)—positive if measured in opposite direction; negative if measured in the same direction

study. He used the line between nasion and basion, projected onto it the condylion, the opisthocranion, and the prosthion, and formed indices n-co/n-op and n-pr/n-op. These indices are given in our Table 12. It should be noted that some fossil forms are included in the table, which makes this compilation of particular interest to us. There is a clear distinction beween man, including fossil man, on the one hand, and the australopithecines and the great apes, on the other. Plesianthropus stands about halfway in both indices. We have not included Schultz's data on embryos and juvenile forms, which form an essential part of his contribution, but only his general conclusion regarding the position of the condyles. He points out that in embryos and juveniles the condyles are generally further forward than they are later in adult life. He ends his study with this query: Why has the joint between head and spine come to lie so far forward early in the development in simian primates if this specialization is not retained by the great majority of species and if it is of clear advantage for only one species—man? Another study of the location of the condyles by a slightly different technique was made by Ashton and Zuckerman (1952). They oriented the skull in the Frankfurt Horizontal and projected the opisthocranion, the prosthion, and the lowest point of the condyles onto it, erecting a perpendicular from the highest point of the skull and projecting onto it the upper orbital margin and the opisthocranion. They worked out the indices for the position of the condyles, for the height of the opisthocranion, and for the height of the superior orbital margin. It appears that by the first index, Plesianthropus could be classified with the apes; by the latter two, with man. The inclusion of the face—by measuring from the prosthion—marks, of course, a definite change from the procedure of Schultz and accounts for the different result.

In another study Ashton and Zuckerman (1956) have given data on several indices of the articular fossa in man and the anthropoid apes. Unfortunately, these data are not quite clear, and the indices are unaccountably given in millimeters. The standard errors of the means are, moreover, so large that most of the differences are in reality insignificant, although they look quite impressive at first sight. We will not reproduce these data here.

In the earlier study Ashton and Zuckerman (1952) make this remark: "The fact that conspicuous age differences occur in the value of the condylar position index in the great apes, in spite of an apparent absence of any striking differences in the gait of young and adult great apes, or in the way they carry their heads, makes it possible that inferences about the carriage of the head derived from a study of the precise values of the condylar position index in an isolated skull may be misleading. In other words, the position of the foramen magnum may be determined by other factors than merely by the position of the head, and the indices are not as meaningful as we might expect them to be at first sight." Thus, in the final analysis, they come to the same conclusions as Schultz.

Cranial capacity is, of course, of particular interest to us. Table 13 contains the raw data for the four great apes, for the most part

TABLE 13

CRANIAL CAPACITIES OF PRIMATES (IN CC.)

| PRIMATE | AFTER SCHULTZ (1947) | | AFTER ASHTON (1950) | |
| --- | --- | --- | --- | --- |
| | Male | Female | Male | Female |
| Hylobates...... | 104.0 | 100.9 | ................ | ................ |
| Orangutan..... | 423.6 | 365.6 | ................ | ................ |
| Chimpanzee.... | 392.7 | 354.1 | $399 \pm 7.0$ | $366 \pm 6.5$ |
| Gorilla........ | 531.7 | 458.0 | $543 \pm 4.3$ | $461 \pm 5.4$ |
| Man.......... | 1,450.0 | 1,350.0 | ................ | ................ |

from Schultz (1947). Since brain weight does not increase in direct proportion to body weight, it is hardly permissible to compare brain weights directly. The graph which Schultz uses elsewhere (1950) to compare body weight and brain weight gives a better picture, but even there the fact that brain weight increases only as the 0.65 power of body weight is not taken into account. The few figures which we were able to extract from the literature are perhaps none too good, but they at least tend to show that the brain weight stands in a very different relation to the body weight in different forms, a fact almost completely hidden by the raw figures. It is also of interest to see that most apes have a brain weight roughly proportional to 0.30 of the adjusted body weight, the chimpanzee 0.60, and man 0.95. (Body weight is "adjusted" by taking into account the effects of over- and underweight.) The difficulties of computing the constant become insurmountable when we come to fossil forms. The australopithecines' relative brain weight, in particular, cannot be determined since nobody knows how much the animals weighed.

Bailey, von Bonin, and McCulloch (1950) were able to discover only little about the brain weight of the chimpanzee but somewhat more about the cranial capacity of the animal. What was known was put together, with different observers arriving at quite different determinations of capacity. Whether this was due to differences in the material or to differences in the technique is impossible to say; all we can do at the moment is to state these differences and to say that the cranial capacity of the chimpanzee can be given as between 368 and 425 cc. for the male and between 337 and 389 cc. for the female.

To discover the cranial capacity of the orangutan, Schultz (1941) measured 47 females and 52 males; Gaul (1933) measured 59 females and 36 males; and a few additional animals were measured by other authors, none of whom measured enough animals to supply reliable means and standard deviations. Schultz and Gaul arrived at values which were quite close for the males but which showed an uncomfortable divergence for the females. Nonetheless, Schultz pooled all of the measurements to arrive at his means for the large series which he used in his study of the orangutan (1941). We are not quite sure whether that procedure was justified. Assuming a standard deviation of 80,* we obtain a difference between the means of 3.5 for the females and of 1.2 for the males, as shown in Table 14. A difference of 3.5 is uncomfortably large.

Schultz (1940) made an interesting study of the size of the eye and the orbit, which extended to numerous primates, including prosimiae; a few examples of his results are given in Table 15. The curve which is obtained when all the material is pooled is fairly smooth and follows fairly closely the curve which is obtained for cranial capacity or for brain weight. This is, after all, to be expected since both eye and brain follow the same type of

---

\* The standard deviation of 80 is a rounded-off figure derived from standard deviations of various anthropoid series (Bailey, von Bonin, and McCulloch, 1950).

growth, and all primates rely on their eyes to about the same extent.

Man is the only mammal that does not possess sinus hairs; anthropoid apes show them above the eyes and on the lips (Henneberg, 1914). It is impossible for us to say how sinus hairs

### TABLE 14

#### CRANIAL CAPACITY OF ORANGUTAN (IN CC.)

| Sex | After Schultz (1941) | | After Gaul (1933) | | Differ- ence* |
|---|---|---|---|---|---|
| | Number of Cases | Average Capacity | Number of Cases | Average Capacity | |
| Female....... | 47 | 336.6 | 59 | 389.8 | 3.5 |
| Male........ | 52 | 416.4 | 36 | 434.1 | 1.2 |

\* Difference of means in terms of standard deviation.

### TABLE 15

#### BODY WEIGHT AND RELATIVE SIZE OF ORBIT AND EYE IN SEVERAL PRIMATES*

| Primate | Sex | Body Weight (in Kilo- grams) | Relative Size of Orbit | Relative Size of Eye |
|---|---|---|---|---|
| Hylobates.......... | F | 5.3 | 0.18 | 0.08 |
| | M | 5.7 | 0.17 | 0.08 |
| Orangutan......... | F | 37.5 | 0.059 | 0.04 |
| | M | 74.6 | 0.036 | 0.006 |
| Chimpanzee........ | F | 44.1 | 0.061 | 0.016 |
| | M | 48.9 | 0.054 | 0.012 |
| Man.............. | F | 54.9 | 0.039 | 0.015 |
| | M | 66.1 | 0.040 | 0.013 |

\* After Schultz, 1940.

differ in their sensitivity from ordinary hairs. Sinus hairs receive their innervation below the insertion of the arrector pili muscle in contrast to ordinary hairs, which have their nerves above the insertions of these muscles. That all nerves around the hairs have a sensory function is obvious. Histologically, sinus hairs have sinuses around their roots below the insertion of the arrector pili muscles, hence their name. In the connective tissue which forms the walls of these sinuses, numerous nerves enter which form complicated nets and rings. Tretjakoff (1910) saw complicated *Schaltapparate*—intercalated structures—which may conceivably have been due to the fact that the connective tissue shrinks more than the nerves, although this is admittedly a little farfetched. It may be that in man the sensitivity of the skin is so well developed that special organs for finer discriminations are no longer necessary. In addition, man's head is not necessarily the first part of the body that comes into contact with the surrounding world but rather the hands, and perhaps for that reason, the sinus hairs on the head have been lost. Whatever the reason, this difference between man and all other mammals is of interest. Histologically, the hairs of the eyebrows and moustache do not resemble sinus hairs (Frédéric, 1904–5).

To sum up, we can say this: None of the living primates is in the direct ancestral line of man; they are all side issues, as it were. This conclusion is clear from a consideration of the vertebral column. The fact that man has a longer tail than any other primate is of importance in this connection. While some forms have a higher number of vertebrae than man, others have a lower number and have therefore overshot the mark of man, so to speak. The pelvis and the configuration of the promontory, which are intimately connected with the posture of the organism, show man to be rather far removed from the rest of the great apes. The intermembral index, too, suggests that man did not come from brachiators. The changes in the foot and in the inguinal region can be explained as adaptations to the upright posture of man. Upright posture, together with the additional fact that man probably has a much greater sensitivity than the primates, may also account for the lack of sinus hairs. The pattern intensity in the palm of the hand and to a lesser extent in the sole of the foot shows again that man is not at the end of a phyletic line that includes the living primates.

On the whole, then, the great apes should only be used with extreme caution for any phylogenetic speculations.

# CHAPTER II

# The Fossil Forms

Before we can discuss the evolution of the brain, we must get to know the fossil forms with which we have to deal and their relationships as far as they can be unraveled. We shall confine ourselves to the Hominidae. Since quite a number of accounts of fossil men have appeared lately, by Le Gros Clark (1955), J. Piveteau (1957), A. Gieseler (1959), G. Heberer (1960), and others, it will be unnecessary to give another detailed account of their anatomy and their culture. We shall concentrate on an analysis of their endocasts.

## Australopithecus

We begin with the Australopithecinae, among which we shall recognize two forms, Australopithecus and Paranthropus, following the classification of Robinson (1956) but deviating from Le Gros Clark (1955). According to Robinson, Australopithecus was a meat eater, while Paranthropus was a vegetarian. He deduces this from the dentition.

The first find of Australopithecus was made in Taungs in British Bechuanaland just over the border from the Transvaal. It was found on the western slope of the Harts Valley in the lime works of Baxton in the cliffs which form the eastern end of the Kaap plateau; the cliff had been worked back about two hundred fifty feet. The fossil was in a brown pocket of breccia, which evidently had been washed down from the overlying veld. In this region, Neville Jones, in the early 1920's, had found numerous implements dating up to the Chellean age, and so the possibility of finding human remains had always appeared good. The Taungs skull was found during operations in a lime work about 1924, after a baboon skull that had for some time been on the mantle shelf of the manager of these works had been delivered, through Josephine Salmons, into the hands of R. A. Dart, of the University of the Witwatersrand in Johannesburg. The identification of the baboon skull stimulated further search for primate material and led finally to the discovery of the famous Australopithecus youth, the Taungs skull. Dart has only recently told of his long fight for the recognition of the Australopithecus (Dart, 1959), and the account need not be repeated here. Further finds were made from 1936 on at Sterkfontein, Swartkrans, and Kromdraai, northwest of Johannesburg, and from 1945 on at Makapansgat, about two hundred fifty miles northeast of the places just mentioned. The first three sites are within about two miles of each other (close to the town of Krugersdorp) in a region that is now rather dry and has few trees. The hills in which the caves are situated are only about one hundred to one hundred fifty feet high. The caves are to a large extent filled with breccia, in which the fossils were embedded. The breccia was investigated in great detail by Brain (1958). The caves were being filled up during the early Pleistocene period; Sterkfontein, Swartkrans, and Makapansgat belong to the first interpluvial, Kromdraai to the second interpluvial (Brain, 1958). On all the evidence it appears that Sterkfontein is the oldest site, Makapansgat the next, and Swartkrans the youngest of the three.

The fact that three caves (Sterkfontein, Swartkrans, and Kromdraai) which are so near to each other have yielded three different types of fossils is partly explained by the fact just alluded to, namely, that the caves belonged to different geological periods. But the tendency of Broom, who excavated these sites, to split species should also be taken into account. In fact, Le Gros Clark (1955) is inclined to think that all Australopithecinae belong to the same genus, if not actually to the same species.

At Swartkrans, Broom (1952) found *Paranthropus crassidens,* a form that is a little bigger than Plesianthropus and has a definite crest on the skull and probably crests on the occipital bones as well. He found two adult and two children's skulls, all of them imperfect. The first, a female skull, has a large part of the brain case intact, and thus an estimate of the cranial capacity could be made—about 750 cc. according to Broom. The second skull, also supposed to be female, is preserved only in its anterior part; its cranial capacity is given by Broom as 800 cc. He notes that behind the auditory opening there is a large mastoid, larger than in most human skulls. Why this should then be a female skull is not quite clear since a larger mastoid is generally characteristic of male skulls.

The skull of one of the children, badly crushed but intact for the greatest part, was found early in 1950. It was judged to be male, about 7 years old. The first premolar is about to be shed, the permanent incisors are intact, and the permanent canine has not yet erupted. The cranial capacity of this child was judged to be about 750–800 cc., which may be a little high. The skull of the second child, of a probable age of 13 years, is badly crushed; it is supposed to have had a capacity of about 700 cc.

At Sterkfontein, Broom, Robinson, and Schepers (1950) found what they called Plesianthropus. This fossil appears to have been about the size of a small man, say a Bushman, and according to his pelvis, walked upright. The skull has no crests, only moderate ridges.

Broom, Robinson, and Schepers (1950) describe the following skulls from Sterkfontein (numbers correspond to those given in the memoir):

No. 5. The skull of an adult woman, almost complete, but without lower jaw and teeth, which Broom called *Plesianthropus transvaalensis*. It was found in a large piece of breccia which was blasted on April 18, 1947; the blast divided the skull into an upper and a lower half, thus exposing the inner sides and enabling Broom to study the endocranial side as well. Its capacity is given as about 480 cc.

No. 6. A very imperfect female skull, with the brain case in very bad condition.

No. 7. One-half of the face and almost the whole of the right side of the brain case of a skull. The occipital region seems to be crushed and deformed, as are the parietal and temporal regions. The capacity has been estimated at about 500 cc.

No. 8. Part of the top and part of the base of a skull, as well as some fragments between the two sections. The whole posterior fossa including the foramen magnum is preserved, but the estimate of the cranial capacity is necessarily only very approximate, and not much value can be attached to it.

The site at Kromdraai finally yielded *Paranthropus robustus* (Broom and Schepers, 1946); finds to date have consisted mostly of limb bones, very important in themselves but not for our purposes. The somewhat broken talus, in particular, made it again fairly clear that the Australopithecinae walked upright.

Still another type of fossil man, which Dart (1948) called *Australopithecus prometheus* from the mistaken idea that the black discoloration found in the so-called Cave of Hearts was due to fire, was found at Makapansgat. This site has so far not yielded a complete skull but only a part of an occiput. However, the parts of the pelvis which have been found there indicate again that Australopithecus walked upright. As only a small part of the whole breccia has been searched thoroughly, we may well be in for further surprises.

In his paper on the occipital fragment from Makapansgat, Dart gives a number of measurements, such as the endocranial height and the greatest parietal width, which are clearly no more than educated guesses. He also points out the numerous Wormian bones (small intercalated bones within the cranial sutures, especially in the lambdoid suture), which he considers to be a human characteristic. He compares the fragment from Makapansgat with the Paranthropus skull in which the occiput was missing. By using the reconstruction of Schepers, he obtains a good fit for Makapansgat and arrives at a cranial capacity of 650 cc. If this were a female brain, then the male of this type would have a brain weight greater than that of a Pithecanthropus—and that in a creature which weighed perhaps 80–100 pounds.

Similar finds have been made in Laetolil, in East Africa, and in Sangiran, in Java, where they have been named Meganthropus. That these finds really belong to the genus Australopithecus has been shown by Robinson (1953, 1955).

A study by Schepers (Broom, Robinson, and Schepers, 1950) of the endocasts of the Australopithecinae is an excellent example of the way in which overenthusiasm can lead to completely untenable conclusions. Schepers goes into great detail, but his analysis, especially of the sulcul pattern, has gone astray and results in the most fantastic interpretations. He goes to great lengths to identify and locate the central sulcus (properly identified in the text, although called the postcentral sulcus in his illustrative figure). We very much doubt the correctness of Schepers' interpretations.

Schepers gives the lengths of the arcs from frontal pole (FP) to the upper end of the Rolandic sulcus (Rm [medial end point of Rolandic sulcus]), from that point to the parieto-occipital fissure, and from this fissure to the occipital pole (OP). Using these measurements to compute the index FP-OP/FP-Rm (see Fig. 5, p. 53, for location of points), we obtain the following results:

| | | | |
|---|---|---|---|
| Gorilla | 41 | Australopithecus | 44 |
| Orangutan | 36 | Pithecanthropus | 45 |
| Chimpanzee | 39 | Rhodesian man | 39 |
| Plesianthropus V | 38 | | |

These figures are at complete variance with those we obtained some years ago on the brains themselves:

| | |
|---|---|
| Macaque | 54 |
| Chimpanzee | 59 |
| Modern man | 58 |

Since our values were derived from stripped brains, we consider them more reliable and are forced to disregard Schepers' interpretations of the central sulcus.

A few words should be said about the lunate sulcus, which Schepers claims to have recognized on the brain, and which was identified by Dart in Australopithecus. Generally, the sulci of the occipital lobe are so closely invested by the pia and the arachnoid that it is impossible to see them through the dura mater, and we strongly suspect that this is the case here too. Any claim to have identified this sulcus in an endocast must be viewed with great suspicion. We also view with suspicion the claim of Keith (1931) that a depression a little farther forward is due to the lunate sulcus. I am afraid that we must admit that we shall never know for certain.

Concerning the middle frontal sulcus, Schepers states: "The

general anthropoid pattern consists of a strongly marked middle frontal sulcus which commences near the rostrum and courses directly backward to terminate in the precentral sulcus." In the chimpanzee, Bailey, von Bonin, and McCulloch (1950) found that the middle frontal sulcus was inconstant and that it occasionally fused with the fronto-marginal sulcus.

His study of contours is a little more useful. He stresses the somewhat narrow outline of the frontal lobe, and concludes that the horizontal contour of the brain of the South African fossils foreshadows the form of the human brain in a development away from the anthropoid ape brain. In regard to the sagittal contour, no great conclusions are reached, and the vertical contours of the various forms are no different.

Schepers' study of the endocranial vascular patterns leads to long discussions which, however, remain largely sterile. The differences observed seem to be to a great extent purely accidental.

In his chapter on metrical characters, we read that the larger the absolute measurements are, the greater the variability becomes. This is contrary to biometric experience in which variability, as measured by the coefficient of variation, is smaller for over-all measurements and is no greater in man than in the chimpanzee or the macaque. The tables of measurements and indices in this chapter are useful.

The last chapters on more general questions are once more so speculative as to be almost useless from a scientific point of view. It is interesting, though, to cast a glance at the general idea underlying Schepers' work:

> "The emphasis on the specific cephalic development of the Hominidae may even have been overstated by some, as in the case of the concept, originally Elliot Smith's, that the growth and development of the human brain were not merely part of his general anatomical evolution, but that certain changes in the brain actually and inexorably determined the subsequent course of Man's somatic modification and adaptation."

Very few people would venture to agree with this view today.

Judging by the morphology of his pelvis, Australopithecus must have walked upright (Dart, 1949a). Whether he had all of the peripheral apparatus required for the production of speech is not completely clear, but it is possible. The extent to which he had a culture is also not known. No stone implements that can with certainty be attributed to Australopithecus have ever been found, although some of the very simplest implements, such as the Kafuan pebble tools, were found in layers just above the one that contained remains of Australopithecus. Dart (1949a, 1957) has made a case for the use by Australopithecus of bones, teeth, and horn in what he calls osteodontokeratic culture. He maintains that Australopithecus used practically everything as a tool for hitting, scraping, and a thousand other purposes. It has been said that Australopithecus had fire; the Cave of Hearts was adduced as proof of this assertion. But it was later found that the black deposit on which this theory was based was actually the remains of guano from bats, and the claim of the use of fire was silently dropped.

## Sinanthropus-Pithecanthropus

The next group that will be considered is that of Sinanthropus-Pithecanthropus, which has been so well described by Weidenreich (1943) and von Koenigswald (1938). It is now generally agreed that the two forms belong to the same genus, if not to the same species. Their names will be used here as merely descriptive, without implying that the two forms belong to different genera.

The first find of Pithecanthropus was made by Dubois (1894) in 1891–92 in Java. A skull and other bones were found in deposits by the Solo, or Bengawan, River near Trinil. Examination of the fossils that accompanied the human remains convinced Dubois that he was dealing with the late Pliocene period, a dating that is no longer accepted.

Over thirty years elapsed before new finds of a related genus were made; in 1926 Black (1927), of Peking, obtained a human tooth which he described in detail and on which he built a new genus, Sinanthropus. Thanks to the energy of Black, money was found to start excavations on a large scale, and in the thirties numerous new skeletons were found which belonged to the same genus. These finds were described in great detail by Black's successor, Weidenreich (1943).

In the late thirties new finds were made in Java by von Koenigswald (1938). Several skulls were found by the collectors employed by von Koenigswald which were studied by him and by Weidenreich.

The brain of the original Pithecanthropus was described in detail by Ariens Kappers (1929), who went into a minute analysis of all the sulci that he thought he could identify on the frontal lobe of the endocast. It is doubtful whether this claim to correct identification can be upheld; but even if it could be, we would not know much more when we were through than when we began, for the variability of the sulci, especially the frontal sulci, is very high, and their configuration, therefore, means very little for a deeper understanding of frontal lobe functions. Ariens Kappers found 3 frontal sulci, with numerous branches, on the endocast of Pithecanthropus. Whether these were really sulci or were merely slight depressions on the endocast is impossible to say. His contention that the enlargement of his sulcus 4 is an indication of the large development of Brodmann's subregio frontalis inferior cannot be accepted. The subregio frontalis inferior is well developed in all apes; it is the subregio frontalis superior that becomes enlarged in humans. His identification of the lunate sulcus is similarly suspect. He arrived at a brain weight of 972 gm. for the Pithecanthropus from a linseed capacity of 1,000 gm.

Weidenreich (1936) gave a detailed description of the endocasts of the Sinanthropus skulls, in which he rightly pointed out that the casts show very little of the gyral configurations—in particular, that the lunate sulcus cannot be identified on the endocast. He established, on the other hand, that the height-length index (100 height/length of brain) varies considerably from the Sinanthropus-Pithecanthropus group to the Neanderthal group and from the Neanderthal to modern man. Some of his figures for the height-length index in the parietal region are the following:

| | | | | | |
|---|---|---|---|---|---|
| Chimpanzee | 42 | Sinanthropus | 40 | New Britain | 51 |
| Orangutan | 48 | Rhodesia | 48 | Australian | 50 |
| Gorilla | 42 | Gibraltar | 48 | Chinese | 56 |
| Pithecanthropus | 40 | Le Moustier | 49 | Dean Swift | 56 |

Weidenreich is at great pains to point out that the greatest increase in the size of the brain does not occur in the frontal, but in the parietal, region, and argues against the overevaluation of the frontal lobe as strongly as anyone else, including the present author. The geological time in which this form lived is again not clearly established, but following Kurtin (1957), we can put it at about 360,000 B.P. (before the present).

Some limb bones which are ascribed to Sinanthropus have been found in Choukoutien. They differ in nowise from those of modern man, and therefore, the assumption that this race had an upright posture appears reasonable.

While Java man had no tools, so far as we know, Peking man evidently did make some rude tools, such as chopper-like cores and flakes in the shape of points and scrapers. He also appears to have had bone tools, much in the same way as the Australopithecus (Breuil, 1939).

## Solo Man

The skulls of Solo man were found between 1931 and 1941 on the shores of the Solo River, a small river in the central part of Java that flows from the region of Soerakarta first east, then north, and into the Java Sea at the west end of Madoera Island. The river has terraces 2, 7, and 20 meters above the present level of the river bed. It is in the last one, the Ngandong bed, that the fossils were found. The bed appears to belong to the last glacial period, but the dating is evidently none too certain. Although it is not certain when this race lived, it is clear nevertheless that in the evolutionary process it stands between Pithecanthropus and Neanderthal man.

The following skulls were found and described by Oppenoorth (1934) and by Weidenreich (1951):

Skull 1. Almost complete calvarium, said to be from a fairly old female. Capacity *ca.* 1,200 cc.
Skull 2. Frontal bone of a child between three and seven years old.
Skull 3. Defective calvarium of an older individual.
Skull 4. Anterior part of a calotte of a middle-aged female.
Skull 5. A very large and long calvarium with the base broken away. Capacity *ca.* 1,300 cc.

Skull 6. An almost complete calvarium. Capacity 1,175 cc.

Skull 7. Small fragment of the right parietal.

Skull 8. Two parietals.

Skull 9. Calvarium with the greatest part of the base missing of an adult of advanced age. Plaster on the inside of the skull; no attempt to remove it.

Skull 10. Greater part of the base missing except for the sides of the temporal bones.

Skull 11. Almost complete calvarium. No capacity given.

Weidenreich (1951) has given a detailed description of the skeletal material which for the most part goes far beyond what we need to know in this context. The only thing that should be emphasized here is the configuration at the pituitary fossa, which shows that the Solo man had a much wider space between the two temporal lobes than modern man. The width in Solo man was 22 mm.; in modern man it is, on the average, 10 mm. Since the width of the foramen ovale and the dimensions of the foramen magnum are also much in excess of those of modern man (Table 16), we should conclude, not that the pituitary itself was much larger, but that there was a much greater amount of connective tissue around the various structures than there is in modern man.

The mandible from the Mauer sands near Heidelberg need not be discussed here since nothing about the brain can be deduced from the find. It is said to fit into the types of Pithecanthropus and Sinanthropus.

## Neanderthal Man

Neanderthal man has been known for more than one hundred years. The first skeleton that was recognized as belonging to that race came from the little town of Neanderthal, in the valley of the Düssel, about 10 km. east of Düsseldorf. Actually, a skull of the same race had been found in Gibraltar a few years earlier, but it was not recognized as such until after the find in Neanderthal had been published.

Numerous other finds have been added since that time, and we now have almost enough for a statistical treatment of this race. Finds were made in Western Europe—in Belgium, France, Germany, Italy, and Spain—later in North Africa, Palestine, and Russia, and recently in Rhodesia and the Cape of Good Hope in Africa. That these skulls belonged to different "races" as the result of geographical isolation, as postulated by Weidenreich (1941) and Singer (1954), can readily be admitted.

TABLE 16

DIMENSIONS OF FORAMEN OVALE AND FORA-
MEN MAGNUM OF SOLO MAN
AND MODERN MAN*

| SKULL | LENGTH (IN MM.) | WIDTH (IN MM.) |
|---|---|---|
| | Foramen Ovale | |
| Skull 6 (Solo) | | |
| Right............ | 12.0 | 8.2 |
| Left.............. | 9.3 | 6.2 |
| Skull 11 (Solo) | | |
| Right............ | 11.0 | 10.2 |
| Left.............. | 6.3 | 7.2 |
| European male | | |
| Right............ | 8.0 | 8.5 |
| Left.............. | 4.0 | 3.5 |
| | Foramen Magnum | |
| Skull 6............ | 41.0 | 31.5 |
| Skull 11............ | 45.0 | 29.0 |
| Modern man........ | 37.0 | 26.6 |

\* After Weidenreich (1951).

The question whether this group mixed with modern man or whether it became extinct and was replaced by modern man is still not quite settled, although on the whole the latter explanation is the more likely. It has become clear, at any rate, that the earlier representatives of this group were closer to the main stream of human evolution than the later ones, who seem to have been a slightly aberrant type with exaggerated characteristics and who probably died out during the Würm glaciation (Howell, 1951).

The skull of Neanderthal man is large, has very pronounced supraorbital ridges, is a little low in relation to its length, and has a receding forehead and a large face and palate. We do not have to go into further details here; these few indications will suffice to give a general impression.

Endocranial casts of a number of Neanderthal skulls have been subjected to considerable scrutiny. We shall review several of these studies a little more closely.

Weidenreich (1947) has pointed out that the Sylvian fissure is completely closed in the great apes, that in the fossil men it has a slight opening at its beginnings but that in modern man it has no opening. In the fossil skulls there is a corresponding Sylvian crest on the bone which is not found in the great apes or in modern man. This shows once more how careful we have to be when we want to establish phylogenetic trends and, more specifically, that it is incorrect to place the great apes, fossil forms, and modern man in a direct evolutionary line.

The skull from Weimar-Ehringsdorf has been described by Weidenreich (1928) in a monograph which contains very little information about the brain. No endocast was made. The skull was found in a number of pieces which did not fit together very well, and Weidenreich had to attempt a reconstruction. His way of putting the pieces together should be mentioned, since it obviously influenced the capacity of the skull. Between the pieces (there were four or five of them) he left fairly large gaps; nowhere did he fit them closely together. Whether this was correct or not is hard to say, particularly when one has not seen the original. But the impression somehow remains that the reconstructed gaps between the bones are larger than they were originally, and therefore, that the capacity given for this skull—1,450 cc.—is too large and probably should be corrected down to some extent.

The endocast of the man from La Chapelle aux Saints was described in great detail by Boule and Anthony (1911). In their paper, remarks can also be found about the endocasts of other Neanderthaloids as well as about many other skulls of men and apes. In La Chapelle aux Saints the greatest length was 185 mm.; the greatest breadth 145 mm.; the basiobregmatic height of this skull

126 mm.; and the whole height of the brain 155 mm. The height-length index (100 height/length) was thus 68.1.

Boule and Anthony also investigated the relief of the middle meningeal artery, which will be discussed more extensively later on. According to these investigators, the anterior ramus is of less importance in the anthropoids than in man. In the man from La Chapelle aux Saints, the anterior ramus appears to be rather simple. Boule and Anthony then launch into a detailed discussion of the sulci and gyri of the brain in their specimen from La Cha-

TABLE 17

FRONTO-ROLANDIC, PARIETAL, AND OCCIPITAL
INDICES FROM SEVERAL ENDOCASTS

| SKULL | FRONTO-ROLANDIC INDEX* | | PARIETAL INDEX* | OCCIPITAL INDEX* |
|---|---|---|---|---|
| | Superior | Inferior | | |
| Modern man....... | 53.3 | 43.3 | 25.3 | 21.2 |
| La Chapelle........ | 52.3 | 43.7 | 21.4 | 26.5 |
| Chimpanzee........ | 55.9 | 39.2 | 19.6 | 24.2 |
| Orangutan......... | 55.5 | 39.2 | 21.3 | 23.2 |

\* Measurements according to Cunningham, 1892.

pelle. Many authors have felt that such a detailed survey really goes beyond what one can legitimately see on endocranial casts, and we agree with them.

In Table 17 we give some indices describing the size of the frontal, parietal, and occipital lobes of some forms. These indices can be compared with similar values given on pages 54 and 55.

Boule and Anthony point out that none of the lobes of the brain is a logical unit, but that every one of them has several functions. We would subscribe in principle to this conclusion, although their manner of expressing it is perhaps too much in the vein of the older ideas of localized functions (we shall come back to these questions later). Their remarks about the seat of articulate language are also too greatly tinted by ideas that have not been able to survive.

The brain of the fossil man of La Quina has been studied by Anthony (1913). His paper contains a host of measurements not only of this brain but also of numerous other brains. We will mention here only those that seem to be of particular importance —especially the index of the height of the brain. If we compare the height with the length in the usual fashion by forming the index, 100 height of the brain/length, we obtain the following indices:

|  |  |
|---|---|
| La Quina | 32.0 |
| La Chapelle | 35.7 |
| Neanderthal | 38.0 |
| Gibbon | 26.2 |
| Gorilla | 31.7 |
| Chimpanzee | 35.5 |
| Orangutan | 32.1 |
| Modern man | 42.5 |

Schwalbe (1899), who used a different base line, obtained the following values:

|  |  |  |  |
|---|---|---|---|
| Pithecanthropus | 34.2 | La Chapelle | 40.5 |
| La Quina | 39.1 | Spy I | 40.9 |
| Gibraltar | 40.0 | Spy II | 44.3 |
| Neanderthal | 40.4 |  |  |

The gradual increase in height is clear. Anthony also measures the lowness of the brain in other ways, such as by determining the angle of the frontal lobe and the height of the brain at the bregma. Further details seem unnecessary at this point.

The endocranial cast of Rhodesian man was investigated by Elliot Smith (1928), who wrote the official description of this part of the skull. He points out that so far as the form is concerned a close analogy can be found with the brain of Neanderthal man, although the Rhodesian skull is considerably smaller than all Neanderthal skulls with the sole exception of the Gibraltar skull. He finds a precocious development of the orbital region, a defective development of the frontal and the parietal regions, and a good development of the posterior temporal region. It may also be of interest to note Smith's discovery that the broadest point in the Rhodesian brain is in the region of the temporal lobe and not, as in most modern men, in the region of the parietal lobe. The cranial capacity of Rhodesian man was 1,280 cc.

A detailed survey of the fissures of the frontal lobes of Neanderthal endocasts was made in 1929 by Ariens Kappers. He found the fissuration of Neanderthal man more humanoid than that of Pithecanthropus but different from modern man in the following respects: Neanderthal man reproduces the fissures more correctly on the endocast than modern man; he shows a strong development of the middle frontal sulcus and perhaps a lesser development of the inferior frontal convolution. We can only point to the criticisms of Symington (1916), who found that the relief of the endocast bore little resemblance to that of the underlying brain.

The Saldanha skull was found in 1953 on the farm "Elandsfontein," about ten miles from Hopefield near Saldanha Bay, north of Cape Town (Singer, 1954). Ronald Singer (1955) and Keith Jolly found the skull as a number of fragments in the sand over an area of about 16 square feet. They were able to reconstruct the skull vault, using twenty-three out of the twenty-eight fragments.

The complete skull—which, thanks to the kindness of Professor Singer, I was able to see on a visit to Cape Town—is remarkably like the skull of Rhodesian man: from glabella to lambda the two are almost identical; in the occipital region the Rhodesian skull shows a slightly greater bulge than the skull from Saldanha. The Saldanha skull has a slightly more receding frontal bone and is a little higher than the skull from La Chapelle aux Saints, but the difference is almost negligible. The results of my examination will be reported in this study in due course. A detailed description of this endocast has not yet appeared.

The Galilee skull was found in 1925 in a cave close to the foothills that delimit the plain around the Sea of Galilee. In a shelter in which implements had been found on the surface, systematic diggings were performed which led to the discovery of a second cave, Mugharet-el-Zuttiyeh, a little higher up a valley, which yielded fragments of a human skull. In a highly detailed description of these fragments, Arthur Keith (1925) devoted considerable space to the endocranial cast. The skull, which is probably female, belongs to the Mousterian period and is clearly that of an individual of the Neanderthal type. Only the frontal bones and parts of the sphenoid have been preserved, but there is enough to make the study of the endocast worthwhile.

The first thing that strikes one (although Keith does not lay stress on it) is the pronounced "keel" of the orbital surface of the brain when viewed from the front. The orbital surfaces make a deep hollow, so that the medial portion projects like the keel of a ship—a much more pronounced projection than in modern man. That the eyes sit higher in the brain cavity than in modern man may be deduced from the presence of this keel. But this is our interpretation and not part of Keith's analysis. The height of the brain from presphenoid to the internal bregma measures 88 mm. in the Galilee skull, 77 mm. in the Gibraltar cast, and 91 mm. in the cast of an Australian aborigine. The temporo-bregmatic height is 110 mm. in the Galilee skull, 92 mm. in the Gibraltar skull, 100 mm. in the Rhodesian skull. The cranial capacity was judged by Keith to have been about 1,400 cc. Keith goes into a detailed survey of the frontal convolutions of the brain in which we do not intend to follow him; the interesting thing for our study is that he appears to think that the upper part of the frontal lobe increases more than the lower one, which is in accord with the present author's thinking about this matter.

The question of the posture of Neanderthal man has agitated people considerably since Boule maintained that he walked with a stooping gait, slouching on slightly bent knees with his head and shoulders bent forward. If we carefully go over the available material, as Patte (1955) recently has done, we find that very little of Boule's assertions can be substantiated and that in all likelihood Neanderthal man walked with the same upright posture as Homo sapiens.

As we will see, the ability to speak depends not only on the development of the brain but also on the development of the peripheral apparatus—the position of the larynx, the size and shape of the pharynx, and the form of the mouth cavity. It is almost impossible to get any accurate idea of the first two factors in Neanderthal man, but we can get some idea of the shape of the mouth cavity from the shape of the mandible. We find, then, that the mandible of the Neanderthaler allows about the same amount of room for the tongue as that of modern man, who can speak, and therefore, from that point of view, there is no reason to deny the ability to speak to that race. The position of the larynx would depend on the way the head was carried on the cervical spinal column, and owing to the great movability of that part of the spine, it is almost impossible to deduce the carriage of the head from the form of the vertebrae. But some indication may be obtained from the position of the foramen magnum, and we find here that its position is not so very different in the Neanderthal man from that of modern man. (A paper by Ashton and Zuckerman [1952] makes it clear that the position of the foramen magnum in Neanderthal man is close to modern man and far removed from the anthropoids and from Plesianthropus.) All in all, we are probably justified in ascribing the faculty of articulate speech to the Neanderthaler.

As to the culture of the Neanderthaler, we find a definite and well-characterized stone industry. Both cores and flakes were used, and among their tools were choppers, side scrapers, and triangular points. There is indirect evidence that they used wooden spears. A human skeleton was found with a deep wound through the femur and pelvis, and round balls of stone have been found which are thought to have been missiles. The Neanderthaler was a fearless hunter, even going after the mammoth and the bison. He used the phalanges of the bison as chopping blocks or anvils but does not seem to have mastered the technique of working bone; he merely used what was handy. He evidently had fire, frequently lived in caves, and probably wore animal pelts against the cold. Some of the Neanderthalers' skeletons were buried, such as the one found at La Chapelle aux Saints, and fine flint implements and portions of bison have been found with the skeletons. Thus, it appears that they had some idea of a future life for which provision had to be made. In a cave in Monte Circeo a skull of Neanderthal type was found within a circle of stones with the foramen magnum artificially enlarged. One may assume that the brain had been taken out and eaten (see Oakley, 1957).

## Upper Paleolithics

Finally, we come to the Upper Paleolithics, which are, to all intents and purposes, modern men. We have numerus skeletons from this period; some of the most important are the skeletons from Les Eyzies, the descriptions of which were originally published by Broca (1868), the skeletons from the Grotte de Grimaldi near Monaco, the skull from Chancelade (Morant, 1928), the skeletons from Obercassel near Bonn, the youth from Aurignac, and the skulls from Předmost and Krapina. It will be clear from this enumeration that we are against splitting up the Upper Paleolithic population into several races, as has frequently been done. On the whole, we follow Morant (1930), who bases his judgment on reliable biometric criteria and not on vague impressions or morphological judgments that can not be sustained by more rigorous methods. There are a few minor differences between the Upper Paleolithics and most modern races, but they are probably of no more than racial significance. Thus the foramen magnum is both longer and broader than it is in modern man, and the skull capacity is greater than it is in almost all modern races by about 40 to 50 cc. These are about the only differences that even very careful biometric research can unearth (Morant, 1930).

It will be useful to include here a discussion of a few skulls which belong in time to an older stratum but which, in their general appearance and in their measurements, are clearly the forerunners of modern man.

The Steinheim skull was found on July 24, 1933, and has been described by Weinert (1936). It was found in a gravel pit near Steinheim a. d. Murr, a tributary of the Neckar, not too far from Stuttgart. It lay about 7 m. below the surface, covered by 5½ m. of gravel and 1½ to 2 m. of loess; under the skull were about 9 m. more of gravel. In this layer there were also remnants of *Elephas antiquus, Rhinoceros mercki,* and *Rhinoceros hemitoechus,* as well as a giant stag with broad shovel-like antlers. Above this, there was a layer of gravel belonging to the period of *Elephas primigenius.*

According to Weinert, the skull was deformed from lying in water for a long time where it had become soft and malleable. It is evidently a female skull; it has fairly large supraorbital tori but otherwise looks quite like a modern skull. We forego here a detailed anthropological description, since this is not within the province of this paper, but merely call attention to the capacity of the skull. The following values are given by Weinert:

| | |
|---|---|
| After Froriep............. | 922 cc. |
| After Welcker............ | 1,163 cc. |
| After Lee-Pearson........ | 1,184–1,214 cc. |
| After Manouvrier......... | 1,239 cc. |
| From the endocast........ | 1,070 cc. |

The last value is, incidentally, the only mention of the endocast of this skull. The mean of the computed values is 1,145 cc., which may well be not far from the mark, since the low value of the endocast can be explained by the fact that not all of the adhering stone and sand could be removed from the inner surface before the measurements were made.

It might be added that a short time after his article describing the Steinheim skull appeared Weinert (1936) declared in a note in the same journal that by an oversight his article was published prematurely and that he should have waited for the publications of Berckhemer (1937, 1938) and Gieseler, who had actually discovered the skeleton.

The next fossil to be mentioned is the skull from Swanscombe, a small village between Dartford and Gravesend on the south side of the Thames (Swanscombe Committee, 1938). The skull was found in two pieces: the occipital bone on June 29, 1935, and the parietal bone, in the same layer, on March 15, 1936. The two fitted perfectly; thus there can be no doubt that they belonged to the same individual, who is judged to have been female. The skull was found in a layer of the hundred-foot terrace which is ascribed to the Middle Acheulean period.

The detailed comparisons of this specimen—and of the Steinheim skull—carried through by Morant in the official report indicate that these two skulls can safely be considered to be of the modern type, clearly distinguishable from the Neanderthal type.

As the study of the Swanscombe endocranial cast reveals, the brain is somewhat ill-filled. The bones are of rather extraordinary thickness, but their shape is quite modern. The capacity of the skull was about 1,325 cc. There were numerous markings on the endocast which, however, according to Le Gros Clark (1955), cannot be clearly identified with any sulcus. In particular, the presence of a lunate sulcus cannot be ascertained.

The culture of the Upper Paleolithics shows a distinct improvement over that of the preceding period. The stone tools are often very well executed and of fine workmanship. The Upper Paleolithics also used bone tools, many of which have come down to us. They are frequently decorated with drawings, incised on them, which depict scenes of hunting and the like. But their greatest claim to fame is, perhaps, the paintings which are found on the walls of caves, frequently in very inaccessible places deep inside the caverns. Nobody fully understands these drawings. Breuil, among others, has advanced the idea that the paintings may have had a magic significance, that they were supposed to bring luck to hunters. The important point is that they definitely had beliefs of a quasi-religious nature and were on the road to a higher culture.

We particularly want to mention the interesting hypothesis of Dart (1959) that speech developed along with fishing. He believes that this occupation needed a fairly complicated collaboration among numerous people that could not have been achieved without articulate language.

We cannot go into any further details about fossil forms here, but we do not want to pass up this opportunity to mention the work by Abbé H. Breuil (1939), the studies by von Eickstedt (1952), and the monograph by A. Laming (1959) on the cave of Lascaux.

# CHAPTER III

*The Endocasts*

What can legitimately be deduced from endocranial casts about the brains which they purport to portray? Much that we have gathered from the literature is of little value, since it is based on mistaken premises and homologies which can hardly be expected to survive a more critical examination.

We shall turn our attention first to cranial capacity, which takes up so much room in most discussions largely, we suspect, because it seems to be easy to measure. Cranial capacity is supposed to be a good indicator of the brain weight and thus of the development of the brain. Obviously, given the specific gravity of the brain and its volume, the weight of the brain can be deduced by a simple formula. According to Danilewski (1880), the specific gravity of the brain in man is 1.041. But the capacity of the cranial cavity is not in a constant ratio to the volume of the brain since the brain diminishes in weight in old age, and the size of the cranial cavity may increase in size as the result of the reabsorption of the inner table; thus, to compute the maximum weight of the brain from the capacity of an older individual may not be as easy or as reliable as it looks at first.

In comparative studies, the further difficulty arises that the ratio of white to gray matter changes from species to species. And since the white matter is a little heavier than the gray, the value of 1.041 is probably not true for all forms. Even with these preliminaries out of the way, the subject still bristles with difficulties.

First of all, the determination of capacity is in itself not easy. The late Wingate Todd (1927) once said that an error of 40 cc. in either direction by the seed or water method would not be unusual.* While it can be hoped that the errors would cancel out in a longer series, this is by no means certain, and it is, moreover, a commonplace that no series can be more trustworthy than its individual measurements. Todd devised a method to measure the capacity with a plastic substance, but so far as we know, it has not been generally adopted. The technique of taking capacity has been reviewed by Tildesley and Datta-Majumder (1944), who discussed in great detail the personal equation of different observers. They find a standard deviation of 7.5 cc. per 1,000 cc. of capacity between Macdonell and von Bonin and of 6.7 cc. per 1,000 cc. of capacity between B. Hooke and von Bonin. Thus the gloomy outlook of Wingate Todd appears unjustified.

What exactly do we know once we have measured the cranial capacity or the weight of the brain? Certainly, the weight of the brain is a very poor indicator of its functional value. Some years ago, the present author (1934) put together all we knew about the capacities of the various races and found that there was no apparent correlation between the average cranial capacity and the cultural status of a race. Moreover, in any major series of skulls, the capacity will vary between, say, 1,800 and 1,200 cc. without a corresponding correlation with any known psychological character. Still it has been said that a certain amount of brain is necessary for the normal functioning of an individual. Keith (1948) has spoken in this connection of a cerebral Rubicon, which he put at 800 cc.; only when the cranial capacity is greater than this amount are we justified in assuming a human intelligence and that ability to learn which appears necessary for human status. Dart (1956) has tried to show that the strict adherence to this value—calling anything below 800 cc. infrahuman and anything above it manlike—is unjustified by quoting a num-

* In the seed method, the skull is filled with mustard or similar seeds in a standard manner through the foramen magnum. Care has to be taken to tamp the seed down with the same force in all skulls and to be sure to fill the skull completely, particularly in the anterior and posterior fossae. In the water method, water is poured into the skull with the same precaution as far as the anterior and posterior fossae are concerned. The skull may have to be dipped into paraffin first to insure that all the holes are closed tightly and no water can run out. In either method, after measuring about ten skulls, a crâne étalon should be filled to insure constancy.

ber of examples of human beings with brains that were far below this arbitrary standard. He cites examples of Bantus with a capacity of 511 cc., 519 cc., and 561 cc. who were able to function in a human way as herd boys and farm hands. Another example he gives is of a Bantu woman with a capacity of only 340 cc. who was able to do some routine work and even danced when she heard music. While Dart has thrown quite a lot of dust over the question of brain weight, it must be admitted that the slavish adherence to a cerebral Rubicon, wherever we put it, is similarly misleading. The large brain weights of 2,350 cc. (of Byron and Cromwell) which Dart cites are just as abnormal as the small ones which he adduces on the other side.

All this does not prove that the average weight of the human brain must be greater than the average weight of the brain of a gorilla; it only shows that the brain of man is built in some way different from that of a gorilla and that the internal organization of the human brain* does not change even if for some reason the actual weight of the human brain is far below the average. That it is of some importance that the human brain weight be near the average is shown by the fact that, after all, the possessors of the small brains cited above were idiots or at least feeble-minded. Occasionally, even in modern man, the capacity may be very low. Although in most such cases there is a definite pathological condition as the basis for low capacity, one can occasionally see individuals who seem fairly normal but who have a brain weight below Keith's Rubicon of 800 cc. In the literature there are brain weights of 340, 407, 424, 460, and 490 cc. Some of these are marked as "idiots"; others are given without comment. These observations show that in individual cases the weight of the brain may be extremely low, but do not alter the fact that most people

* By internal organization we do not mean such things as the cell-gray coefficient (the relative amount of space occupied by the perikarya in the cortex, which appears to be merely a function of the size of the brain), but rather such things as the amount of glia, the connection of the glia with the nerve cells (the ratio of small to large cells in the cortex), the threshold of the cells for stimulation, and so on. For none of these qualities have we any estimate.

have a much greater brain weight and that the average is about 1,400 cc.

There is another difficulty here. When we start with the brain weight of, say, the macaque, then go on to the chimpanzee, the orangutan, and the gorilla, and thence proceed to Australopithecus, Pithecanthropus, and Neanderthal man, we mix modern forms with extinct ones and obtain a series which, strictly speaking, represents nothing that ever happened, that is partly idealistic and partly phylogenetic. For this reason the two lines of development should be kept apart and the anthropoid apes for the moment left out of the account.

A great deal has been written about the cranial capacities of the Australopithecinae, much of it, as we have seen, open to doubt. Attempts have been made time and time again to reconstruct capacities from quite insufficient data, from very partial remnants, such as a single occipital or frontal bone. Thus Dart (1948), who, by the way, had harsh things to say about the value of cranial capacities in a later article, devotes considerable space to the evaluation of the cranial capacity of the *Australopithecus prometheus* and arrives, on the basis of an occipital fragment, at a value of 650 cc. He plots coronal contours on square-ruled paper, which look quite impressive until one realizes that the Australopithecus contour is mostly imaginary. Of course, Dart's imagination may have been right, as it so often was, but the contour as given does not correspond to anything he has seen in nature. Some of Schepers' reconstructions (Broom, Robinson, and Schepers, 1950) are similarly suspect.

Dart is entirely right in pointing out that Australopithecus was of much lighter build than the gorilla and, therefore, that even if his brain weight was about the same as that of the gorilla, his coefficient of cephalization (i.e., the ratio of body weight to brain weight in a correlation diagram) must have been considerably higher. An interesting comparison was made by von Koenigswald (1953) in relating the mesiodistal length of the three upper molars to cranial capacity; his table (we are not quite sure of his exact values for the capacities) is given herewith as Table 18. The table shows that cranial capacity increases relative to the teeth from the Australopithecinae and the Pithecanthropinae to man, and that among the various races of man there is quite a high variability in this respect. The low value for the Melanesians is suspect, to say the least, and may have to be thrown out, particularly since the Papuans, who are certainly not far removed from the Melanesians, have a much higher value. Otherwise, the table makes good sense.

TABLE 18

RELATION OF SKULL CAPACITY (IN CC.) TO MESI-
ODISTAL LENGTH OF THREE UPPER MOLARS
(IN MM.)*

| | |
|---|---|
| Plesianthropus | 13.4 |
| Pithecanthropus erectus | 24.3 |
| Pithecanthropus modjok | 25.8 |
| Sinanthropus XI | 34.2 |
| Steinheim | 36.7 |
| Rhodesia | 42.8 |
| Melanesians | 33.1 |
| Papuans | 44.7 |
| Europeans | 47.3 |

* After von Koenigswald, 1953.

TABLE 19

CRANIAL CAPACITIES*

| Skull | Number | Capacity |
|---|---|---|
| Pithecanthropus | 14 | 1,026 mm. |
| Plesianthropus | 4 | 506 mm. |
| Australopithecus | 1 | 500 mm. |
| Paranthropus | 1 | 650 mm. |

* After Ashton, 1950.

We can compare cranial capacities directly. For this purpose, we have used Table 19. The capacities are given by Ashton (1950), who accepts for the most part those measurements given by Broom and Dart, although he rejects some exorbitant claims, as is only right.

Looking over the whole material that we have been able to collect, we can say that during the last 1,000,000 to 500,000 years cranial capacity seems to have increased from about 500 cc. to about 1,500 cc. This sounds like an enormous change, but when it is remembered that during this time man went through about 15,000 generations, it means an increase per generation of less than 1 cc., an amount that would probably go unnoticed. The figure for the increase in capacity may be remarkable, but it is certainly not impossible.

In studying the contents of the cranial cavity, we must not forget that an endocast does not show the brain per se, but the brain wrapped up in the dura mater and thus seen only through a veil, as it were. On the dura one can generally make out the course of the middle meningeal artery quite distinctly, and since that artery has been studied fairly extensively, we should see what we can learn from its configuration.

As is well known, the middle meningeal artery enters the skull through the foramen spinosum and breaks up into two rami, which can be classed as anterior and posterior, sometimes almost at once, sometimes only after running over most of the temporal lobe. In the region of the anterior ramus, one can distinguish a frontoparietal and a bregmatic secondary branch; in the region of the posterior ramus, a superior and an inferior temporal branch. The obelionic branch can come from either ramus. The two main branches can be of roughly the same caliber, or the anterior branch can be the bigger one. The posterior branch is only very rarely bigger.

A fair amount of work has been done on the variations of the middle meningeal artery from two points of view. The clinician has been interested less in the variations than in the exact places where a trephine hole had to be made when the vessel ruptured and a hematoma ensued, a situation which often leads to a compression of the brain. If the artery can be secured in time and the hematoma removed, the life of the patient may be saved. The anatomist has been interested in the variations of the artery and their possible significance from a phylogenetic point of view. In a large number of cases, Chandler and Derezinski (1935) found that the origin of the posterior branch was near the foramen spinosum 338 times (31.5 per cent), near the level of the greater wing of the sphenoid 265 times (24.7 per cent), and midway between these two points 354 times (33 per cent).

Confining ourselves to the anatomical papers, we should cite first of all a study by Giuffrida-Ruggeri (1912), who distinguished between five types of division of the middle meningeal artery (Fig. 4). In Type I, the posterior ramus is small and comes off the anterior ramus quite high, close to the Sylvian fissure; the obelionic branch is part of the anterior ramus. In Type IIa the division of the two main rami is again high, but the obelionic branch comes off the posterior ramus. In Type IIb the division is low, i.e., close to the foramen spinosum, and the obelionic branch comes from the posterior main ramus. In Type III the

TABLE 20

VARIATIONS OF MIDDLE MENINGEAL ARTERY

| Population | Number | 1* | 2 | 3 |
|---|---|---|---|---|
| Chinese (Toida)................. | 192 | 48.3% | 34.0% | 17.7% |
| Japanese (Adachi)............... | 100 | 51.0 | 40.0 | 9.0 |
| Japanese (Akiba)................. | 219 | 43.8 | 53.4 | 2.8 |
| Europeans (Giuffrida-Ruggeri)..... | 119 | 59.6 | 37.8 | 2.5 |
| American Whites (Rothman)....... | 191 | 37.7 | 60.2 | 2.1 |
| American Negroes (Rothman)..... | 212 | 41.5% | 55.7% | 2.8% |

\* 1: R medius and posterior separate.
  2: R medius and posterior have a common origin.
  3: Two medii present.

division is again low, but the anterior ramus is definitely the larger one. In Type IV, the two rami are of about the same size; the posterior ramus comes off near the foramen spinosum. A rare anomaly is the type in which the posterior ramus is the larger one and the anterior ramus is definitely a branch of the posterior. Giuffrida-Ruggeri makes no phylogenetic speculations; he only mentions, almost in passing, that his material from apes and monkeys is quite insufficient and that all his types are found in all human populations.

Rothman (1937) dealt with the material from Washington University in St. Louis by dividing it into three groups as recommended by Adachi (1928). Tabulating all the series that were known at the time of his study, he found the percentages given in Table 20. There are a few significant differences between the series, e.g., between groups one and two of the whites of Giuffrida-Ruggeri and Rothman. Whether the dissimilarity is due to

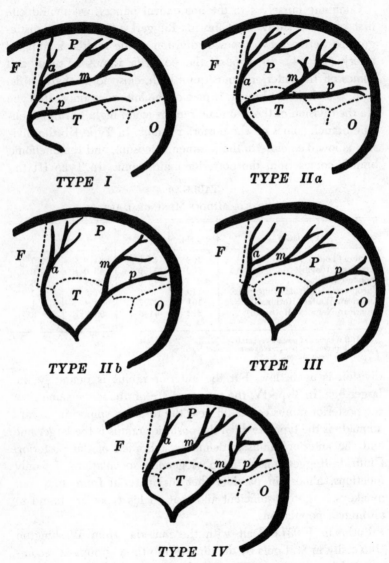

FIG. 4.—Various types of branching of the meningea media. (After Giuffrida-Ruggeri, 1912.)

differences in interpretation or to actual differences is hard to say; at any rate, it is impossible to gauge the phylogenetic significance from this purely human material. Differences of inherited strains appear the most likely explanation.

Weidenreich (1938) published an account of the meningea media in Sinanthropus and other forms which is of interest since he tries—as almost the first—to arrive at a phylogenetic interpretation of his findings. He maintains that in lower forms the anterior ramus is poorly developed and the posterior ramus bears the

TABLE 21

LOCATION OF POSTERIOR RAMUS OF
MIDDLE MENINGEAL ARTERY

| LOCATION OF POSTERIOR RAMUS | PAPIO | | MAN | |
|---|---|---|---|---|
| | Number | Per Cent | Number | Per Cent |
| No posterior branch................. | 19 | $39\pm7$ | ........ | ........ |
| Posterior ramus coming off high...... | 21 | $43\pm5$ | 4 | $4\pm2$ |
| Posterior ramus coming off middle.... | 9 | $18\pm5.5$ | 37 | $37\pm4.8$ |
| Posterior ramus coming off low....... | ........ | ........ | 69 | $69\pm4.6$ |
| Territory supplied by anterior:posterior branch (in arbitrary units)......... | 6:1 | | 2.2:1 | |

brunt of the blood flow. We shall see that our own observations do not support this conclusion.

When I went to South Africa, I spent some time in getting acquainted with the drawing apparatus which I intended to use to draw the contours of some fossil endocranial casts on which I wanted to work. In order to get the feel of the equipment, I drew a number of modern endocasts—a series of brains of the baboon and anther series of modern Hereros. The brains were in the Department of Anatomy of Witwatersrand University, and their middle meningeal arteries had been marked. The information given in Table 21 was gathered from these drawings. I first tried to apply Giuffrida-Ruggeri's (1912) five types but ran into so many difficulties of interpretation that I finally gave it up and resorted to the method to be outlined. By a point near the medial longitudinal fissure, I marked out the territory of the anterior and posterior branches as best I could, and then measured the distance to that point, in a straight line, from the frontal and the occipital poles, which may not be as good as measuring an arc but is much faster and sufficiently accurate for a first orientation.

From our table it is perfectly clear that the posterior branch is much more important in man than it is in Papio. This contradicts the statements of the literature—e.g., Weidenreich (1938)—that the posterior branch is less important in modern people. Of course, we do not know whether the pattern found in Papio is really primitive or whether it is a secondary change. Further investigations along the lines suggested here may be of interest, particularly when monkeys and apes are taken into account.

To return to the brain, we can say that it not only becomes larger but also undergoes changes in its form. The brain of Neanderthal man, of about the same size as that of modern man, is lower and not as well "filled out" as that of modern man. This had been observed and measured many times. (A good figure to illustrate this behavior is that given by Weidenreich [1941, p. 379]. The relatively greater increase of the parietal bone is also illustrated in this figure.) This phenomenon was first clearly recognized by Boule and Anthony (1911) and has since received widespread attention in the literature. It is undoubtedly important for the understanding of the evolution of the brain.

It should at last be admitted that most of what has been said and written on the sulci of the brain as they have been seen on endocasts is worth very little. Symington (1916) compared casts with the actual brains they pretended to portray and found that very little of the surface of the brain could actually be seen in the casts. Using European material, he showed that there was little besides the Sylvian fissure, the superior and middle temporal sulci, and the orbital sulci that could be identified in the casts. In 1925*a*, Keith published a detailed account of the brain of Piltdown man which involved a survey of the various sulci in which he stressed the third frontal convolution and the parts around the Sylvian fissure. In 1928, Elliot Smith published his account of Rhodesian man. In 1911, Anthony published the description of the endocast of the man from La Chapelle aux Saints; and in

1913, an account of the fossil brain of La Quina. A review of his works appeared in 1928. All of these have been considered here and, on the whole, found wanting. Le Gros Clark, Cooper, and Zuckerman published a paper in 1936 on the endocast of the chimpanzee. They carefully prepared the six brains they had by blacking them and rubbing off the black from the higher parts of the cast. They found that one could infer very little from the cast about the disposition of the sulci, that, in particular, the lunate sulcus was not made visible on the cast, and that the central sulcus was generally not recognizable.

In 1949, Packer compared the cast with the corresponding brain of an Australian aborigine. Again, the sulcal pattern was poorly marked on the cast; a number of grooves did not coincide with sulci of the brain. Very little, therefore, could be inferred from the cast regarding sulci. Much of the older work by Keith, Elliot Smith, and Anthony has to be disregarded.

Are we able to determine the way in which the brain grows in phylogenesis? We have sufficient data on two parts of the brain in monkeys and in man to get some idea—the parietal and the frontal regions. We shall consider the parietal association field. That this may be a misnomer is at the moment beside the point. What we want to point out is that the field is quite small in monkeys, gets bigger in anthropoids, and is very large in man. These facts are, of course, well known. But it does not appear to be sufficiently realized that the main addition is right in the center between the somesthetic, the acoustic, and the visual fields; that it is, in other words, not a peripheral addition but a growth by intercalation. We can even go into a little more detail and point out that the somesthetic field in the monkey comprises both upper and lower parietal lobules and in man only the upper one. The former assertion is based on the strychnine experiments by the late Dusser de Barenne (1924) and on the investigations of the thalamocortical relations by Walker (1938) and Le Gros Clark and Boggon (1935). The latter assertion is based on the observations of the living human brain by Foerster (1936). We can make out a similar case for the frontal lobe. It is often maintained that it is the third frontal convolution that has been added in man; but if we look at the cytoarchitectural picture, we see that the areas of the third frontal convolution are present in both the monkey and in man. FCBm and FDΓ, the two cortical areas on the third frontal convolution of man, are easily recognized in both forms. It is again the part above the third convolution, i.e., an "associational area," that is enlarged in man. There is the same intercalation as in the case of the parietal lobe. Incidentally, this makes much of what has been written about the third frontal convolution and the speech centers in fossil man, their presence or their absence, and so on, of rather doubtful validity.

The growth of the cortex by intercalation is thus fairly well established. It is in keeping with the ideas expressed years ago by Dart (1934) on the evolution of the neocortex, for which he proposed a dual origin both from the hippocampal and the prepyriform regions. The newer parts, he suggested, were intercalated between the older ones.

In order to determine a number of measurements which might shed further light on the evolutionary changes which the brain undergoes, we have tried to adapt Economo's (1930) encephalometric scheme to our purpose. On the endocasts of fossil skulls, we have attempted to determine a number of encephalometric constants which, while admittedly crude because the landmarks are ill defined, still appear to be better than the attempts by previous authors to determine the impressions of sulci which, even when known, are of doubtful significance (Figs. 5 and 6). We have tried to visualize the upper (Rm) and the lower (Rop) ends of the central sulcus and the location of the parieto-occipital incisure (pom). Neither of these points can be located unequivocally on the endocast, but the position of Rm and pom can be inferred within a few millimeters by elevations due to the veins entering the superior sagittal sinus. The lower end of the central sulcus has to be guessed at. The Sylvian or lateral fissure is generally fairly clear in the beginning of its course, and the point we are looking for is not far behind the tip of the temporal pole. We also need the location of the Cap of Broca (cap), which is easily found as the point on the frontal lobe about opposite the temporal tip. The inferior parieto-occipital sulcus (ipo) has to be

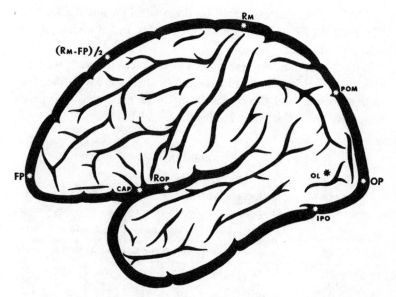

Fig. 5.—Encephalometric constants (lateral view). (After Economo, 1930.)

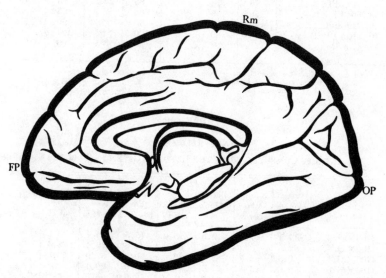

Fig. 6.—Encephalometric constants (midsagittal view.) (After Economo, 1930.)

guessed at, but this can again be done within a few millimeters. The frontal (FP) and occipital (OP) poles are, of course, determined on the cast.

With this in mind, we can glance at the measurements we were able to collect on the fossil brains. We shall start with the Australopithecinae and the brains from China and Java. The pertinent data are collected in Tables 22 A and B.

### TABLE 22A

#### ENCEPHALOMETRY

ABSOLUTE MEASUREMENTS OF AUSTRALOPITHECUS AND SINANTHROPUS

| Encephalometric Lengths (in mm.)* | Australopithecus | Plesianthropus | Pithecanthropus I | Sinanthropus loc E | Sinanthropus loc E I | Sinanthropus loc E II | Pithecanthropus II |
|---|---|---|---|---|---|---|---|
| 1. OP-pom......... | 30 | 28 | 40 | 38 | 32 | 30 | 26 |
| 2. pom-Rm........ | 40 | 32 | 35 | 63 | 50 | 68 | 54 |
| 3. Rm-FP.......... | 105 | 100 | 130 | 110 | 130 | 125 | 110 |
| 4. OP-FP sag...... | 175 | 160 | 205 | 211 | 212 | 223 | 190 |
| 5. OP-ol.......... | 30 | 30 | 50 | 60 | 60 | 40 | ...... |
| 6. ol-Rop......... | 58 | 55 | 70 | 65 | 60 | 70 | 125 |
| 7. Rop-FP......... | 70 | 70 | 85 | 83 | 95 | 85 | 70 |
| 8. OP-FP lat...... | 158 | 155 | 205 | 208 | 215 | 195 | 195 |
| 9. Rm-ipo......... | 50 | 75 | 75 | 90 | 78 | 90 | ...... |
| 10. (Rm-FP/2)-cap... | 80 | 80 | 98 | 100 | 93 | 107 | ...... |
| 11. Rm-Rop....... | ...... | ...... | ...... | 90 | 105 | 100 | 85 |

* 1–4   Sagittal arc and subdivisions.
  5–8   Horizontal arc and subdivisions.
  9–11   See Figs. 5 and 6, p. 53.

### TABLE 22B

#### ENCEPHALOMETRY

INDICES COMPUTED FROM THE LENGTHS GIVEN IN TABLE 22A

| Indices | Australopithecus | Plesianthropus | Pithecanthropus I | Sinanthropus E | Sinanthropus E I | Sinanthropus E II | Pithecanthropus II | Modern Man |
|---|---|---|---|---|---|---|---|---|
| (100×1)/4... | 17.1 | 17.5 | 19.5 | 18.0 | 15.5 | 13.7 | 13.6 | 19.6 |
| (100×2)/4... | 22.6 | 20.0 | 17.5 | 30.0 | 23.6 | 28.4 | 28.4 | 20.7 |
| (100×3)/4... | 60.3 | 62.5 | 63.0 | 52.0 | 60.9 | 57.9 | 58.0 | 59.7 |
| (100×5)/8... | 19.0 | 19.4 | 21.4 | 28.8 | 28.0 | 20.4 | ...... | ...... |
| (100×6)/8... | 36.6 | 35.4 | 34.3 | 31.2 | 28.0 | 35.8 | ...... | ...... |
| (100×7)/8... | 44.3 | 45.0 | 41.4 | 40.0 | 44.2 | 43.6 | 35.8 | 41.0 |
| (100×9)/8... | 31.8 | 48.1 | 36.7 | 43.2 | 36.3 | 46.2 | ...... | ...... |

It should be clearly understood that both lengths OP-FP, sagittal as well as lateral, are taken on points which can easily be identified on the cast and are not subject to doubtful evaluation, whereas the points Rm and Rop are, of course, not clearly to be recognized on the cast. With this in mind, it is clear that the brains of the Australopithecinae are smaller than the brains of the Pithecanthropus group, although the difference is not as great as one might have suspected at first. The real interest lies, of course, in the relative development of the various parts of the brain, and the second part of the table (Table 22B) gives some pertinent data. The most important and the most obvious change that the brain undergoes during these stages of phylogenesis is an increase in the relative height of the cerebrum. This has been pointed out again and again, and details have been worked out by Weidenreich (1941).

It would be very interesting to know whether there are any changes in the width of the pituitary fossa, since this would give a measure for the development of the temporal poles, but unfortunately this region is preserved in so few brains that no conclusions can be drawn.

If we look at the indices—first considering the more reliable ones, namely, the indices 3/4 and 7/8—we see that the frontal lobe of the fossil forms differs but little in size from that of modern man. The frontal lobe of the fossil forms is relatively as large as that of modern man and larger than that of the macaque. It is, of course, to be remembered that, after all, the point Rm is not well defined, and thus a slight discrepancy should not worry us unduly. The result is all the more gratifying. The occipital and the parietal lobes are more difficult to evaluate, since both the points pom and Rm are ill defined and any errors in measurement might be cumulative. But here, too, we find that the trend is in the right direction. If we form an index out of the depth of the parietal lobe, Rm-ipo, and the horizontal circumference of the brain, we obtain values for the fossil forms which are rather different from those for modern man and even smaller than those for the macaque. Here again the uncertainties of the points to which measurements are taken may enter the picture, but the great expansion of the parietal lobe which occurs during anthropogenesis is impressive.

In the Neanderthalers (Tables 23 A and B), the picture changes quite considerably. The occipital lobe remains about the same relative size, although not necessarily of the same composition as regards the functional value of the cortical areas, but the parietal lobe appears to increase at the cost of the frontal lobe. Whether this change is a real one or merely due to a differ-

TABLE 23A

ENCEPHALOMETRY
ABSOLUTE MEASUREMENTS OF NEANDERTHALERS

| Encephalometric Lengths (in mm.)* | Sal-danha | Rho-desia | Gibral-tar | Neander-thal | La Cha-pelle aux Saints | La Quina | Le Mous-tier |
|---|---|---|---|---|---|---|---|
| 1. OP-pom......... | 45 | 40 | ....... | 30 | 53 | 50 | 28 |
| 2. pom-Rm........ | 65 | 48 | ....... | 93 | 51 | 60 | 98 |
| 3. Rm-FP.......... | 130 | 130 | ....... | 125 | 140 | 141 | 140 |
| 4. OP-FP sag....... | 240 | 218 | ....... | 248 | 244 | 251 | 266 |
| 5. OP-ol........... | 40 | 45 | ....... | ....... | ....... | ....... | ....... |
| 6. ol-Rop......... | 85 | 80 | ....... | ....... | 153 | 142 | 145 |
| 7. Rop-FP......... | 80 | 95 | ....... | ....... | 87 | 92 | 100 |
| 8. OP-FP lat....... | 215 | 220 | ....... | ....... | 240 | 234 | 245 |
| 9. Rm-ipo.......... | 115 | 90 | ....... | ....... | ....... | ....... | ....... |
| 10. (Rm-FP/2) cap... | 85 | 105 | ....... | ....... | ....... | ....... | ....... |
| 11. Rm-Rop........ | ....... | 117 | ....... | ....... | 113 | 97 | 115 |

* See note to Table 22A for further identification of these measurements.

TABLE 23B

ENCEPHALOMETRY
INDICES COMPUTED FROM LENGTHS GIVEN IN TABLE 23A

| Indices | Saldanha | Rhodesia | Neander-thal | La Cha-pelle aux Saints | La Quina | Le Mous-tier | Modern Man |
|---|---|---|---|---|---|---|---|
| (100×1)/4... | 19.8 | 18.5 | 13.4 | 21.9 | 20.1 | 11.5 | 19.6 |
| (100×2)/4... | 27.2 | 22.5 | 37.2 | 21.7 | 23.8 | 36.9 | 20.7 |
| (100×3)/4... | 54.0 | 60.0 | 50.4 | 56.4 | 56.1 | 51.6 | 59.7 |
| (100×5)/8... | 18.7 | 20.4 | ....... | ....... | ....... | ....... | ....... |
| (100×6)/8... | 39.5 | 36.2 | ....... | ....... | ....... | ....... | ....... |
| (100×7)/8... | 37.2 | 43.0 | ....... | 36.2 | 39.3 | 40.7 | 41.0 |
| (100×9)/8... | 53.3 | 47.8 | ....... | ....... | ....... | ....... | 53.2 |

ence in the estimates of the site of the central sulcus is debatable. But the fact that it is consistent and that the same relative smallness of the frontal lobe appears in the horizontal measurements makes us believe that it is real, although the difference in the horizontal measurements is not as large as in the sagittal ones.

In the Upper Paleolithics (Tables 24 A and B), we encounter almost the same conditions as in modern man, except perhaps for the fact that the brains are larger on the whole than those of modern man, as exemplified in this table by the area of the frontal

TABLE 24A

ENCEPHALOMETRY
ABSOLUTE MEASUREMENTS OF UPPER PALEOLITHICS
AND COMPARATIVE SERIES

| Encephalometric Lengths (in mm.)* | Cro-Mag-non | Galley Hill | Pred-most 3† | Pred-most 4† | Pred-most 9† | Pred-most 10† | Modern Man | Chim-panzee | Ma-caque |
|---|---|---|---|---|---|---|---|---|---|
| 1. OP-pom.... | 60 | 34 | .33 | 30 | 50 | 33 | 68.4 | 29.1 | 22.7 |
| 2. pom-Rm.... | 60 | 49 | 70 | 80 | 78 | 78 | 56.9 | 29.8 | 16.4 |
| 3. Rm-FP..... | 154 | 164 | 153 | 153 | 146 | 145 | 147.0 | 84.9 | 75.5 |
| 4. OP-FP sag.. | 274 | 247 | 256 | 263 | 274 | 256 | 246.3 | 143.8 | 84.6 |
| 5.,6. OP-Rop... | 154 | 140 | 150 | 145 | 146 | 140 | ...... | 135.2 | 91.7 |
| 7. Rop-FP.... | 96 | 116 | 100 | 100 | 110 | 95 | 93.8 | 51.7 | 32.8 |
| 8. OP-FP lat... | 250 | 251 | 250 | 245 | 256 | 235 | 229.0 | 143.4 | 85.9 |
| 9. Rm-ipo..... | ...... | ...... | ...... | ...... | ...... | ...... | 122.0 | 71.6 | 43.0 |
| 10. (Rm-FP/2)-cap........ | ...... | ...... | ...... | ...... | ...... | ...... | 85.0 | 57.0 | 31.4 |
| 11. Rm-Rop.... | 125 | 106 | 125 | 125 | 120 | 116 | 105.6 | 71.4 | 40.3 |

* See note to Table 22A for further identification of these measurements.
† After Gorjanović-Kramberger, 1906.

TABLE 24B

ENCEPHALOMETRY
INDICES COMPUTED FROM LENGTHS GIVEN IN TABLE 24A

| Indices | Cro-Magnon | Pred-most 3 | Pred-most 4 | Pred-most 9 | Pred-most 10 | Modern Man |
|---|---|---|---|---|---|---|
| (100×1)/4...... | 21.8 | 12.9 | 11.4 | 18.3 | 12.8 | 19.6 |
| (100×2)/4...... | 21.8 | 27.2 | 30.3 | 28.6 | 30.4 | 20.7 |
| (100×3)/4...... | 56.4 | 59.9 | 58.3 | 53.1 | 56.8 | 59.7 |
| (100×5 and 6)/8. | 61.5 | 60.0 | 59.0 | 56.0 | 59.5 | 59.0 |
| (100×7)/8...... | 38.5 | 40.0 | 41.0 | 44.0 | 40.5 | 41.0 |

lobe. But the indices for the various parts of the brain do not differ greatly from those of modern man.

We are inclined to consider the aberrant values of Neanderthal man as a sign that he was indeed a side issue that later became extinct. The fact that the later Neanderthalers were further removed from the mainstem of human evolution than the earlier ones points in the same direction.

# CHAPTER IV

# On the Structure and Function of the Cortex

By and large, we have established as well as one can with the small amount of material at hand—and with the difficulties of defining the points of measurement on the endocast—that the pattern of the brain has not altered significantly from macaque to man and that only the Neanderthaler falls slightly outside the range established by the other forms. So far, so good. But what does this add up to in terms of function? How much can we infer from this about the mental faculties of the bearer?

It is hoped that the following somewhat detailed account of the cortex may prove of use to the physical anthropologist if he should wish to try to correlate the dry bones of human paleontology with the gradual ascent in human culture. It should be made clear at the outset that we do not intend to give a detailed account of the mental development of man such as the one recently attempted by Lassek (1957). We do not feel able to undertake this task.

The measurements on which we have reported cannot give a detailed picture of the brain in terms of its function. In the first place, all of the lobes are of mixed function. Thus the frontal lobe consists, as is well known, of the somatomotor sphere and the so-called prefrontal field, which has an entirely different function that is only imperfectly understood. The percentage of these two parts differs in different forms, from the small primates to man, and not much can be said about the function of the frontal lobe as such. The same is true of the occipital lobe, i.e., that part of the cortex which lies behind the parieto-occipital fissure. In the macaque, not to go too far down in the scale of primates, this region is almost completely occupied by the visual area; in man, the visual area barely extends onto the lateral side of the lobe. We know that the parietal lobe has at least two spheres, the somatosensory and the parietal association areas, whatever that may mean. The temporal lobe has an acoustic and an associational region, and Broca's "grand limbique" is concerned with emotions and similar states. These examples should be sufficient to call for extreme caution in interpreting our results. It certainly is not as simple as one might wish.

In the second place, it is not at all clear how far we can ascribe various functions to the different lobes of the brain. It seems fairly obvious for the simpler functions, such as the reception of the various sensory stimuli or the sending-out of motor orders—although even here we might run into more difficulties than we bargained for. But the higher functions, including speech, cannot be localized so easily, and for that reason, too, the size of the subdivisions may not be very enlightening.

In order to clarify this question, we shall have to look at the theories of the cerebral cortex as they have developed during the last century or so. The older ideas about the cortex can be found in Kleist's monumental work (1934) which analyzed the experiences derived from the study of war wounds on the German side during the First World War. According to Kleist, every part of the cortex has its peculiar function, and it is the harmonious working-together of all these parts that insures a healthy mental life. This scheme goes back to Franz Joseph Gall, and was given a seemingly secure anatomical foundation by Brodmann (1909), Campbell (1905), and O. and C. Vogt (1919). While Kleist was elaborating it for perhaps the last time, other workers had gone far toward demolishing this edifice.

Kleist defines his purpose in the Afterword:

The object of a new interpretation of brain pathology meant, as far as anatomy and localization was concerned, to find the proper counterpart in the new architectonic ideas about the brain for the clinical disturbances. We had to take into consideration not only the architectonics . . . , but also the various layers of the cortex, the different functional importance of which had been shown by Cajal, Kappers, etc. . . .

While Flechsig taught that next to the motoric and sensory fields there existed large associational fields, among which he differentiated a frontal, a parietal, and a temporal field, we maintain that the cortex consists principally of sensory regions. The occipital region is optic; the temporal, acoustic; and the centroparietal, haptic, with the last region being connected with a gustatory field in the subcentral region (and perhaps also in the insula). The frontal region is a labyrinthine-myesthetic field; the orgitocingular field is a region of inner sensations (ego); the pyriform and ammonic fields are devoted to smell. In each region there are a sensory zone proper, a motor zone, and a psychic zone, and also mixed zones.

It is also of basic importance for the functional plan of the brain that infracortical parts participate strongly in the psychic functions and disturbances. Apart from a critical psyche responsible for the personality, which is made up by character and gifts, there are the essence as the totality of psychic functions of the diencephalon and the basal ganglia, the state of wakefulness and sleep as functions of the diencephalic central gray, and attention and consciousness as functions of the mid- and hind-brain.

It is enough to give these indications. Kleist's book contains many valuable contributions but also much that is vitiated by the underlying philosophy which in several instances has been proved wrong.

In Germany, Goldstein (1927) published an account of localization in the cortex in Bethe's *Handbuch der Physiologie,* which was based on the Gestalt theory of psychology and stressed that the cortex always worked as a whole and not in some mosaic fashion as the older theories had advocated. A lot of good and useful work was done along these lines, e.g., on the structural alteration of the visual field after scotomata or hemianopsia. Such studies did not help to unravel the morphology of the cortex since they bypassed anatomy. Von Weizsäcker (1947) went still further in the direction of Goldstein in his "Gestaltkreis" theory, which admittedly did not want any anatomy. But here again numerous new facts were found.

In America at about the same time, Lashley (1929) published a book, *Brain Mechanisms and Intelligence,* which also advocated the consideration of the cortex as a whole and was based on numerous experiments on rats. Lashley points to interference patterns as the next sequence to sensory impressions, admitting that the excitation must come again to a focus in the motor sphere.

Individual differences are again mentioned—the handwriting of an individual, for example, is just as characteristic whether he writes with his right or his left hand, with his foot or with his mouth. Lashley bases many of his considerations on the work of Lorente de Nó (1949), who showed that the cells of the cortex have a wide range of connections and that their activity may well spread over large parts of the cortex. In this work, Lorente de Nó merely assumed excitatory synapses but left out of account the presence of inhibitory synapses as well as the influences of cells which, although too weak to fire other cells, may lead to an alteration of thresholds sufficient to change the spread of impulses through the cortex. Depending entirely on which impulses have the upper hand, either a larger spread or a narrowing of the reach of impulses results. For an example of the latter situation, one may turn to the lack of spread of sensory impulses in the cortex as shown by Mountcastle and Powell (1959).

We do not want to go into a detailed description of the histology of the cortex, but a few remarks may be pertinent. The primate cortex, as that of any other mammal, contains different types of neurons. They have been classed in two large groups: Golgi Type I cells, which send their axons into the white matter to subcortical parts or to other parts of the cortex, and Golgi Type II cells, which have short axons ramifying in the neighborhood of the perikarya and do not leave the gray matter. To the latter belong the "star cells" of Poliakow (1962), who says about them: "With the inclusion of these elements, into the reflex arcs . . . numerous very small microscopic centers are separated in the cortical gray matter." In other words, the star cells break up the mass of cells into a mosaic of small units. We know far too little about them and their variability, but they seem to be more numerous in man than in the lower primates. It may be that here we have a clue to the structural organization of the cortex.

These are the only remarks we want to make at this time about cortical histology, but it will also be helpful to get some idea how the various sensory impressions and their characteristics are brought to the cortex. For each sensation, we have three main characteristics. There is the peculiar quality of the sensation to either a visual impression or an acoustic one, and so on. There is, secondly, the locus of the sensation, very clearly perceived in the visual and somesthetic system, less clearly perceived in the acoustical and olfactory systems. And finally, there is the intensity of the sensation. How can we account for these differences?

About the first point, we can say next to nothing. How the pips that are transmitted to the cortex give rise in one case, say, to a landscape, in another to the *Fifth Symphony* of Beethoven, is a mystery that is beyond the confines of neurophysiology. As for the second point, the local sign of a sensation is largely given by the exact location in the cortex in which the signals arrive. This is obvious for such sensory modalities as the optic and somesthetic. Thus, the topographic arrangement of the cortical retina mirrors (with some distortion) the peripheral retina, and the somesthetic field on the postcentral convolutions mirrors (again with some distortion) the body surface. In the acoustic sector, the topography is used to determine the height of the perceived tone. What the topographic arrangement means for olfaction we do not clearly know. The third characteristic, the intensity of the stimulus, seems to be transmitted largely by the rate of firing, although in the case of a complicated *on, on-off,* and *off* stimulus to the inhibitory cells in the cortex the relationship may actually be more complicated than that.

That there is a point to point correspondence between the lateral geniculate body and the striate area is now well known, and the details need no elaboration here (see Polyak, 1957).

From the photoreceptors in the retina to the cells in the striate area there are cells that respond to an *on* stimulus, to an *off* stimulus, and to an *on-off* stimulus. It is not clear yet whether these cells' behavior is innate or whether it depends on the topographic relationship between the stimulus and cell. A second point of importance is that the optic impulses fall continually on different parts of the retina owing to small but continuous movements of the eye. This seems to be very important for avoiding an undue adaptation of the receptors which might lead to an inability to perceive anything. Third, it should be borne in mind that there are over one hundred million rods and cones in the eye but only about one million fibers in the optic nerve, and so only about 1 per cent of the information that reaches the retina is actually transmitted to the brain.

The first point can but need not be interpreted as leading to a sharper contrast between light and dark parts of the visual field. This seems to happen in the receiving field of the superior quadrigeminal body of the frog (Maturana *et al.*, 1960).

Although this arrangement gives, of course, some inkling of the way in which vision comes about, it is still far from satisfactory. Thus we have no idea how color is perceived. The old ideas of Henschen (1930) that there are light and color cells in the striate area is certainly too simple. Anthing we sense is due to processes between nerve cells and not to an impingement of any one cell on another.

In order not to separate things which obviously belong together, we should at this point treat the field of the pulvinar intergeniculatus (area 18), which, as is well known, is in intimate connection with the striate area. In Foerster's (1936) experience, stimulation of the striate area gives rise only to sensations in black and white; it is only when the parastriate area is stimulated that color vision comes about. Although this is certainly no proof for localization, it appears none the less possible that color vision is mainly located in the parastriate area or at least that this area is needed in these processes. It would make sense, then, that the color vision of man appears to differ from that of such forms as the macaque or the cebus monkey, not to mention the chimpanzee (Grether, 1939, 1940).

There is at the present time some difficulty about the functional role of the para- and the peristriate areas. In the marmoset, the visual area may actually include the areas OC, OB, OA, and PFG of Peden and von Bonin (1947) (Woolsey, 1958). This was determined by response to photic stimulation. In the monkey, according to Lashley (1948), there is little reason to consider the visual sector as consisting of more than the striate area proper. Experiments involving the extirpation of the para- and the peristriate areas have led to no recognizable defect in the visual field, such as loss of memory for seen objects or disturbances in the recognition of movements. The same condition seems to exist in the rat, in which only destruction of the visual area proper leads to any disturbances of vision. On the other hand, von Monakow (1895) asserts that the intergeniculate pulvinar is already present in the mouse—that it is, in fact, the oldest part of the pulvinar. In man, stimulation during an operation of the parastriate area gives rise to the seeing of (generally moving) objects, sometimes formed, sometimes no more than fiery balls or shooting flames (Foerster, 1936). The destruction (by trauma) of the parastriate area leads to an inability to recognize seen objects—to what is known as psychic blindness. The symptoms have been described so often and so well that it appears unnecessary to repeat them here.

In regard to vision there seems to be a difference in the organization of the human and the monkey brain. In man, the visual sector evidently takes up much more of the cortex than in the macaque. This may be related to the fact that in man the para- and the peristriate areas together are about three times as large as the striate area (Filimonoff, 1932). It may be in the parastriate areas that we have to look for the increase in importance of vision in man.

The next field that we will consider is that of the nucleus ventralis posterior, the end station of the somesthetic radiation. In the cortex, this radiation comes to the postcentral convolution, which is the somesthetic region par excellence.

Foerster made extensive stimulations of the cortex and arrived at a map which is very similar to that obtained by Marshall, Woolsey, and Bard (1945). In the monkey, on the postcentral gyrus, the segments of the body are laid out in an orderly sequence, and any stimulation is referred to a particular part of the body. The sequence is the usual one: the face is the lowest, then the arm and the trunk, and finally, near the upper border and partly extending over on the medial side of the brain, the lower extremity. The hand and foot take up a comparatively large space in their respective fields, and within these fields the thumb and great toe occupy a similarly disproportionate part.

With the stimulating electrode, it has been almost impossible to evoke during operations "normal" sensations; one generally gets a sort of criblure, like ants crawling over a certain part of the body, or "tingling," or some slight pain, or the feeling that a part of the body is moving. Recently, Powell and Mountcastle (1959) made a detailed study of the postcentral gyrus in the monkey by investigating the evoked potentials of single cells following a peripheral stimulus. In this way they found that area 3, closest to the precentral gyrus, contained a large number of cutaneous and some deep receptors, while the number of deep receptors increased as one went farther back toward the parietal lobe; in all areas, however, there was a mixture of superficial and deep receptors. Receiving cells were found in all parts of the third to the fifth layers of the cortex; sometimes the upper cells were for one modality and the lower ones for the other (of course, we cannot be certain that the investigators always stayed in the same column of cells throughout the thickness of the cortex). It is safe to assume that in respect to the reception of peripheral stimuli the human brain is organized along the same lines as that of the monkey.

In neurology there has always been a tendency to equate proprioceptive and deep sensibility. It is important to keep their differences clearly in mind if we do not want to run into unnecessary difficulties. Proprioception arises in the muscle spindles and is the sensory arm of the two-neuron reflex arc. Most of the incoming messages to the spinal cord go to the motor neurons. A small number of them are (after a synapse in Clark's column) brought via the dorsal spinocerebellar tract to the cerebellum, from which they apparently influence the length of the muscle spindles over the gamma fibers. The story is actually still more complicated, but for the moment it need not concern us. Deep sensibility arises in Golgi's flower-spray endings, the nerve endings around the tendons, the joint capsulses, and so on, and is carried by the lemniscus medialis or the spinothalamic tract to the thalamus and thence to the cerebral cortex. It should be added that deep sensibility is fairly old in phylogenesis, whereas proprioception appears to exist only in terrestrial animals. This conclusion has the corollary that the two-neuron reflex arc is not the primitive arrangement, as is often heard, but a secondary sophistication that arises comparatively late in phylogenesis.

It is interesting and a little puzzling to observe that somesthesis, from its entry into the spinal cord up to the thalamus, is carefully divided into two routes which, moreover, appear to overlap to some extent. The only explanation is again a phylogenetic one; the spinothalamic route is old, whereas the lemniscal route was first laid down in reptiles or mammals. But that explanation only moves the question to another level, for we still do not know why that second pathway was laid down. According to Bowsher (1961) and Mehler, Feferman, and Nauta (1960), the pain fibers end partly in the intralaminar nuclei of the thalamus, whereas touch appears to end exclusively in the ventralis posterolateralis and posteromedialis. In addition, many fibers of the spinothalamic pathway actually go to the superior quadrigeminal body (Glees and Bailey, 1951). The inability to evoke pain from the cortex may be due to the fact that in order to evoke pain at least two loci have to be activated simultaneously or to the fact that pain is actually perceived at the collicular level. At any rate, so far as we know at present, the stimuli coming over the two pathways get thoroughly mixed in the cortex.

It is logical at this point to discuss that part of the field of the pulvinar that is adjacent to the postcentral convolution, in particular, the field above the intraparietal sulcus in man. This region also has to do with somesthetic impulses, although they differ from those received in the postcentral gyrus. On the postcentral convolution, the various body segments are laid out in the well-known sequence; however, on the parietal convolution, there seems to be a sort of global presentation and even some ipsilateral representation, which constitutes, in man at any rate, a second area with quite different characteristics from the first one. So far as we know, the pulvinar does not receive direct somesthetic impulses but only material that has been worked over by the posterolateral nuclei of the thalamus. This is reflected in the quality of the sensations evoked from this region.

Following Critchley (1955), we can ascribe disturbances of the following functions to lesions of the parietal lobe: constructional apraxia, finger agnosia (Gerstmann's syndrome), disorders of the body image, visual defects, and disorders of language and of spatial and symbolic thought. The list is formidable; at the moment, we have no intention of enlarging it and elaborating on the symptoms classified here. It should be noted that many of the symptoms indicate functions which are particularly human or which we find in subhuman primates in only a very rudimentary state.

That the sector of the medial geniculate body is the acoustic receiving area on Heschl's gyrus on the supratemporal plane is of course well known. It deserves to be mentioned that it is no more than a few square centimeters in surface and barely extends over the lip of the Sylvian fissure on the lateral side of the cortex. The sector has a topographic principle: the deep tones are represented on the outside, the high ones near the insula. The details may not be as well known as one might wish, but the general principle is clear enough. It is interesting to remark that if we were to turn the temporal lobe back to the way in which it grew out originally, the low tones would come into the region of the leg in the somatosensory field, and the high tones in the region of the face. Is this why we speak of high and low tones?

In most non-primate brains we find a second acoustic area on which the perception of tones is generally in the opposite direction from that in the first area. We know very little about the secondary acoustic area in primates; in fact, there may be none, or it may be behind the first area, close to the insula—a region that is almost impossible to investigate physiologically. But we do know that the region closest to the acoustic area on the first temporal convolution has to do with the understanding of the meaning of tones, particularly of language. If we should look anywhere for an area especially devoted to speech, we should look here, on the posterior part of the superior temporal convolution. Unfortunately, this part leaves no readily recognizable imprint on the endocast, and thus very little is known about its phylogenetic history.

We shall now go on to the nucleus lateralis intermedius, which receives fibers from the tegmental fascicle of Forel and projects to the precentral region, i.e., to the motor cortex proper. Here begins what in man appears to be the main outgoing pathway from the cortex to the spinal cord. The fields from the various parts of the body are arranged in much the same sequence as in the somatosensory sphere. The famous pyramidal tract is said to have its origin here, from which point it pursues its well-known course into the spinal cord. Actually, it takes its origin from areas 4, 3, 1, and 2 as well as from the parietal fields 5 and 7 and from the precentral fields 6 and 8 (Woolsey and Chang, 1948). Although there is a definite topographic arrangement in the internal capsule and perhaps even in the pes pedunculi, it is lost in the lower levels. From phylogenetic considerations, Coghill (1943) concluded that the first and most important function of the pyramidal tract was to suppress mass movements, which was the original way in which animals moved about or performed other tasks. Only after mass movements had been suppressed did it become possible to execute those fine movements that are apparently under the care of the pyramidal system. That only about 3 per cent of all of the fibers take their origin from the Betz giant cells in the cortex is by now so well known as to need hardly any further emphasis (Lassek, 1954).

We are still insufficiently informed about the way in which the pyramidal tracts end in the cord. We know that the ventral cortico-spinal tract can generally not be followed farther in the cord than about the upper thoracic level, that it is restricted, in other words, to the arm. The lateral tract almost certainly ends, at least in lower forms such as the cat, not directly on the motor cells of the anterior horn, but on internuncials in the posterior horn, from which point the impulses are propagated by several internuncials to the anterior horn cells.

The way in which the pyramidal tract is connected to the final common path appears to vary in mammals. In the cat, about three to four impulses are needed before a motor effect can be observed. In monkeys one or two may suffice, and in man the motor reaction is almost always prompt. Also, the number of stimuli needed may vary with time. At first it may take, say, four impulses to activate the spinal common pathway. If one goes on stimulating, three stimuli and finally two or even one may be sufficient to insure that result. (Bernhard, Bohm, and Peterson, 1953.)

In animals, including most primates, the role of the precentral gyrus appears to be much more modest than in man. We are not certain why this should be so, but when we interfere with the motor cortex proper, most animals, including monkeys, show very little motor deficit, whereas a similar interruption in man is followed by a severe hemiplegia or other appropriate motor deficits. We should remember in this connection that the fields from which the motor impulses can go out to the spinal cord are quite numerous and quite large; in addition to area 4, we have area 6, the postcentral fields (as we saw a moment ago), and also, as we have learned largely from Penfield and Rasmussen (1950), the supplementary area on the medial side of the frontal lobe as well as the second motor area on the infraparietal plane. Whether all these areas are functionally present in monkeys is not known for sure although it is very likely, and it is at least possible that they can compensate for the loss of the "main" area better in lower forms than they can in man.

We next proceed to the field of the lateralis ventro-oralis, which is mainly concerned with relaying impulses from the cerebellum to area 6 (and perhaps 8) of the cortex (to the simple agranular field).

It is, of course, well known that the pyramidal system is supported by the so-called extrapyramidal system in order to work properly and smoothly. The exact relation between the two systems is not quite clear; some workers have gone so far as to deny any difference between the two. Nor is it completely agreed upon what parts belong to the extrapyramidal system. Some people reckon everything to it that is not the pyramidal system proper (Bucy, 1957), while others will allow for the fact that there were older (in the phylogenetic sense) systems which for one reason or another remain intact and still function, although perhaps only in a subordinate role.

We would define the extrapyramidal system proper as those masses (of cells and fibers) that are destined to help the cortex and the pyramidal system in its work. These would include the

basal ganglia, the subthalamic nucleus, the red nucleus, the sub-
tantia nigra, the dentate nucleus, the cerebellum, and the inferior
olive. Apart from the extrapyramidal system, there are two other
motor systems in the brain, namely, the midbrain roof and the
vestibular system. Phylogenetically, the extrapyramidal system
came into being together with the pyramidal system proper, that
is to say, in mammals; the other two systems are much older and
were perhaps already present in fish.

We know very little about the way in which the extrapyramidal
system proper is put together or how it works. Many of its parts,
the basal ganglia, the subthalamic body, the red nucleus, and the
cerebellum, as well as the substantia nigra and the inferior olive
receive impulses from the cortex. The extrapyramidal system has
two outflows, the first one to the cortex and the so-called pyramidal system, the other to the reticular substance and from there
down to the spinal cord. There is every indication that from the
cerebellum and from the globus pallidus impulses go to the ventral nucleus of the thalamus and from there to the cortex, mainly
to areas 4 and 6. Since powerful tracts reach the cerebellum from
the cortex via the pons and via the inferior olive, we have all the
makings of a reverberating circuit that certainly receives minor
additions from the substantia nigra and the subthalamic nucleus
via the globus pallidus.

Probably no system has undergone greater changes during mammalian phylogenesis than the direct outflow of the extrapyramidal system. From the inferior olive there is the olivospinal
tract, which exists in man but which is not known in all its details,
such as exact ending, and so on. There is the rubrospinal tract,
which is large in lower mammals but an insignificant bundle
going no farther than the middle cervical levels in man. There is
finally the reticulospinal tract, which has been demonstrated by
Papez to exist in the cat but which has not been verified in man.
Without going into too great detail, which is impossible in any
case, we can only conclude that the outflow over the cortex as-
sumes increasing importance as we come to man and that the
direct outflow diminishes proportionately in importance. Concerning the nucleus ruber in the cat, we have a very interesting

electrophysiological study by Massion (1961). It seems that both excitatory and inhibitory connections exist between the cerebellum and the nucleus ruber. Since we may assume the same relations for other members of the extrapyramidal tract, the final effect on the anterior horn cells is hard to gauge.

In diseases of the extrapyramidal system one can easily distinguish two kinds. The disease of the substantia nigra and of the globus pallidus causes tremor at rest and rigidity of the cogwheel type. The disease of the cerebellum causes intention tremor and flail-like limbs. One gets the impression that the motor apparatus is held between two reins, as it were, and that that is the reason why in Parkinson's disease the destruction of a nucleus may lead to an amelioration of symptoms.

When we come to the rest of the brain, which is actually a rather large part, namely, the fields of the medial and anterior nuclei, we are on much less secure ground in trying to define functions that could be attributed to these structures. We can only make very general statements. The medial nucleus of the thalamus in man receives its afferents mainly from the pallidum and other basal ganglia and hands them on to the frontal lobe. The vogue for lobotomies of a few years ago has led to many investigations of the projection of the medial nucleus to the frontal lobe (see Meyer, Beck, and McLardy, 1947); thus we are fairly well informed about the anatomy of these relations. The gain in physiological knowledge has not been commensurate; we still know very little about what impulses go to the frontal lobe. That frontal lobotomy was not without its dangers and drawbacks became more and more evident, and it was with relief that many saw therapy turn more and more to pharmacological agents for abolishing anxieties and other symptoms for which frontal lobotomy had been advocated.

The anterior nucleus of the thalamus projects to the medial cortex, in particular to area 24, its anterior part. This nucleus receives its main afferents from the hypothalamus by way of the bundle of Vicq d'Azyr. Again, it is not quite clear what it brings to the cortex, but the recent work of Miller, Galanter, and Pribram (1960) may give some idea. These investigators point out that the medial side of the brain, including the hippocampus, is concerned with the execution of plans rather than with discriminatory functions. The full impact of their ideas is felt perhaps only when one goes through their book as a whole, but even a cursory glance should suffice to bring out the novel view embodied in these studies, which to us appear interesting and intriguing. That the symptoms of deficit of the medial cortex are entirely different from those caused by a deficit on the lateral side is, of course, well known. We have only to remind the reader of the famous syndrome of Klüver and Bucy (1939*a*, *b*) (see also Bucy and Klüver, 1955). After a bilateral resection of the temporal lobe, including the hippocampus and the nucleus amygdalae, in several monkeys, Klüver and Bucy found a hypermetamorphopsia, pronounced oral tendency, and hypersexuality, together with great tameness and occasional restlessness. To narrow down the region from which these symptoms could be evoked did not seem feasible to them.

The sustaining action of the amygdaloid nucleus or the obliteration by this nucleus of certain impulses has been made clear by Gloor (1955) in a number of experiments to which the interested reader may be referred.

But it ought to be clear by now that a survey based on the afferent impulses to the cortex cannot accomplish what it set out to do—namely, give a reasonably complete theory of cortical function. This, in the final analysis, is due to the fact that the various incoming messages are integrated in the cortex and only in that integrated form appear in consciousness. We shall discuss a few problems to which a treatment based on afferent impulses cannot do justice.

Let us begin with language. That language in general is somehow bound up with the region of the first temporal convolution, the inferior parietal lobule, and the third frontal convolution is, of course, frequently stated; but whether some of the different forms of aphasia, such as motor, sensory, semantic, and so on, really exist and are due to lesions of different parts of the "quadrilateral space" or to other factors is not at all clear. On the whole, it appears to be of no value to give a detailed subdivision of the language region. Any subdivision seems to be doomed to failure by the next case that comes along. The fact that Schuell (1960) found language deficit present in all modalities is incompatible with the theories that presuppose a topographic representation of functions in the cortex and with theories that are based on motor or sensory dichotomies.

Control of the movements that are involved in speech is effected in a way rather different from the way in which other movements are controlled. Whereas elsewhere proprioception is the sensory input that guides motor performance, in speech it appears to be mainly acoustic impulses that regulate sounds (Street, 1957).

Conrad (1954) found that aphasia may be caused by lesions in the most diversified regions of the brain—by no means restricted to the quadrilateral space. He could not find any correlation between the site of the lesion and the type of aphasia produced. As is well known, the area of Broca is on the foot of the left third frontal convolution in that part of the convolution that is known as the cap. It was the first region to be connected with speech and is therefore of some historical interest. It was thought to be a particularly human part of the brain for many years, but cytoarchitecture revealed its presence in apes and finally also in monkeys (Kreht, 1936). Of course, these forms cannot speak in the proper sense of that term; but it is clear from stimulation experiments that this area in primates has to do with movement of the larynx and the tongue. This relationship holds for man, too, and in man these organs are important for speech. The question arises whether the area of Broca is essential for speech or whether its extirpation can be borne without enduring impairment of speech. Evidently the question cannot be answered in the same sense for all people; in some cases, a permanent injury to the speech apparatus develops, whereas in other cases no permanent damage occurs. At any rate, several neurosurgeons (Pool, 1949; Penfield and Roberts, 1959; and others) have taken out the area of Broca without affecting the speech of their patients for more than a few weeks. There is no doubt that the importance of the frontal lobe has been vastly exaggerated for a long time. Gradually, we are getting back to a more sober judgment, and the wild claims for the frontal lobe, which, in the final analysis, go back to Franz Joseph Gall, are gradually being reduced to their proper size. This is also true for the speech apparatus, which involves extensive regions in the cortex.

A localization of the speech faculty, if it is possible at all, should take into account first and foremost the temporal lobe. For it is only here, particularly in the acoustic area, that the immediate memory is integrated with the present, as it were. This integration is needed for an understanding of the spoken language and for the possibility of pronouncing not merely a word or two but a whole sentence. What anatomical peculiarities the temporal lobe has to account for this, nobody knows. Almost certainly it is nothing very obvious; but whether it is due to differences in the branching of dendrites or to differences in the number or the arrangement of the glia cells or star cells, or to still something else, is unknown.

The highest integrative functions of the brain were often thought to be located more or less exclusively in the frontal lobes. There is a recent careful study by Chapman and Wolff (1959), which shows that this is not so, and that it is the amount of tissue lost rather than where it is lost that determines whether these functions will be disturbed or not. They give the following list of integrative functions: (1) expression of needs, purposes, and goal-directed activity; (2) mechanisms of goal achievement; (3) capacity of initiating, organizing, or maintaining appropriate and effective adaptive reactions; and (4) capacity to maintain organization during stress and to recover promptly from the effect of stress. These functions do not seem to be bound to any particular part of the cortex but can be disturbed from anywhere. The only necessary condition is that enough of the cerebral mass be destroyed in one way or another. This is well in accord with what Lashley (1929, 1940) and others found in the rat and the monkey and shows that in this respect the human brain does not differ from the brains of lower forms.

# CHAPTER V

## *Conclusion*

The results of our inquiries into the brains of fossil men are somewhat meager: we cannot deduce any details about their mental life—whether they believed in God, whether they could speak or not, or how they felt about the world around them. In this last chapter, we cannot do much more than point to those circumstances which should prevent us from saying too much.

In the first place, of course, the inside of the brain case gives us no more than vague clues about the brain itself. After all, the brain is ensheathed in the dura mater and is thus seen only through a thick veil. In places, we can discern a little more, in other places hardly anything at all, but even in the best of circumstances we cannot see very much. Thus the detailed analyses of the fissuration of the frontal lobes of fossil men that were given in particular by Broom, Robinson, and Schepers (1950) and Ariens Kappers (1929) are probably wrong in the first instance. Moreover, it has been shown in great detail elsewhere (Bailey and von Bonin, 1950) that the fissures of the human brain are quite variable and that these variations do not appear to throw any light on the mental characteristics of the bearer of that brain. For these reasons, we consider the time and effort spent on the fissures of the fossil brains as largely wasted.

That the brain increases in size as we go from the Australo-pithecinae to modern man—or to the Upper Paleolithics for that matter—is quite obvious and, of course, very gratifying. But the meaning of the increase is again not quite clear because, as we all know, brain size as such is a very poor indicator of mental ability. This has been shown best perhaps by Pearson (1925) some years ago. In his series, very gifted persons, such as Léon Gambetta,

Anatole France, or Franz Joseph Gall, had very small brains, of about 1,100 grams. Others equally gifted persons had very large brains; thus Byron and Dr. Johnson had brains of about 2,000 grams. And, of course, some very ordinary persons had equally large brains. So brain size was certainly not very important, and the correlation between brain size and mental capacity was insignificant. But whether this argument can be extended to an evolutionary series is again another matter. For one thing, we know far too little about the bodily proportions of fossil forms. Obviously, the brain stands in a certain relation to the rest of the body, and this rest is still largely hidden from us. Brain size as such is none too meaningful. Moreover, mere size completely leaves out of account the inner structure of the brain, which may be different in different forms and which may determine to a great extent what the brain can do. Whether Dart's ideas about brain size and brain pattern in relation to human status are particularly well taken may be open to doubt. None of the cases of human microcephaly that he cites are, after all, very convincing. All of these individuals were handicapped to some extent, although they were able to get along in simple tasks such as the herding of domestic animals. All this indicates is that, in intelligence, these people were above the animals—hardly very surprising. But humanity would not be on the threshold of annihilating itself by an atomic bomb if it consisted of nothing but the kind of people Dart describes. It is even doubtful that they would ever have found the Australopithecus and wondered about its status.

It appears that most of the forms that we have considered here are built according to the same pattern. But even that may not be quite true, since, for example, the change in the function of the inferior parietal lobe occurs without disturbing the macroscopic pattern. What did the inferior parietal lobule do in fossil brains? In modern man, at least, part of it is devoted to the speech function.

The evolution of speech is generally considered from a somewhat narrow neurological point of view (see Straus, 1961). It is frequently allowed to boil down to the question of whether the third frontal convolution is well developed or not. But it is quite doubtful how far the third convolution of the frontal lobe is actually concerned in the function of speech. Any purely neurological approach, moreover, leaves out of account the peripheral organs which may well have to have a certain configuration before speech can possibly develop.

The changes which the peripheral apparatus undergoes can be brought under two headings: the gradual divorce of the larynx from the choanae and the widening of the mouth so as to give the tongue sufficient room in which to play. About the first type of change, the following remarks are pertinent: in most lower mammals, particularly in macrosmatic ones, the larynx reaches high up into the pharynx so as to make direct contact with the choanae. Thus air can go into the trachea even while the animal is feeding and can go past the olfactory mucosa at all times to give the animal notice of what goes on in the surrounding world. In the microsmatic primates this connection is gradually severed, and the larynx recedes, so to speak, into the neck and no longer makes direct contact with the choanae. This process is not yet completed in most monkeys and reaches its completion only in man and perhaps in the higher apes. It is part of the change which brings the viscerocranium underneath the neurocranium from a position in front of it.

We shall not dwell on the changes that occur in the pharynx, since very little detailed knowledge is available, but rather confine ourselves to the changes that occur in the mouth. The oral cavity in man is broader and gives the tongue more room than in lower forms. This is due partly to the fact that the mandible becomes less massive and partly to the fact that its two rami come together at a different angle, two processes that obviously are related to each other (Fig. 7). All these changes are at least as important as the changes in the brain itself and largely determine whether the individual can speak or not, as Du Brul (1958) and Du Brul and Sicher (1954) have so well stated.

The period in which articulate language appeared cannot be definitely established. All we can say here is that Australopithecus certainly walked upright, as the pelvis shows clearly, and that we thus seem justified in supposing that by that time the larynx had gone far enough into the neck to enable it to play its role in the enunciation of articulate sounds. The mandible, on the other hand, appears still to have been very massive and not well suited to that freedom of movement for the tongue that appears neces-

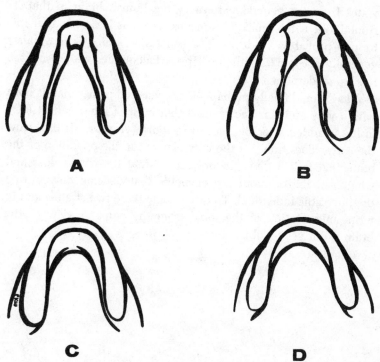

Fig. 7.—Contours of the mandibular body in *A*, Australopithecus; *B*, Paranthropus; *C*, "Telanthropus" (Homo erectus); and *D*, Homo sapiens (modern American white).

sary for the production of articulate sounds. But all this is speculation. For speech to develop, there must be a need for communication between the individual members of a group. Whether these needs were present is anybody's guess. That hunting in packs can be successfully executed with a minimum of communication between the members of the pack is shown by such forms as wolves or lions. Dart's (1959) hypothesis that fishing for food may have been a strong incentive for articulate speech was mentioned earlier, and we want to reiterate it here.

## Conclusion

The fabrication of tools was probably beyond the capacity of Australopithecus, since very few tools have ever been found in close association with him.

We must emphasize again that Neanderthal man evidently deviates from the general pattern of the human brain in that its frontal lobe is too small. This means, as far as I can see, that this form is probably a side issue, a conclusion which is now fairly generally accepted. With the Upper Paleolithics we are on the road to modern man.

What should finally perhaps be emphasized is that man is born with a very immature cortex and that most of what is in it later in life is added after the second to fourth years of his life. How the cortex does things is the only element in the operation of the brain that is laid down before birth; what the cortex does and what man thinks about are elements that develop only during the life of the individual. To disentangle these two strands and to write an evolution of the mind from the point of view of the brain is not yet feasible.

# References and Bibliography

ADACHI, B. 1928. Das Arteriensystem der Japaner. Suppl. to Acta Sch. Med. Univ. Kyoto. Kyoto.

AKIBA, T. 1915. Über die endokranialen Furchen der a mening. med. bei Japanern. Z. Morphol. u. Anthropol., 23:343.

ANTHONY, R. 1913. L'encéphale de l'homme fossile de la Quina. Bull. et Mém. de la Soc. d'Anthrop. de Paris, 6th ser., 4:117–95.

———. 1928. Anatomie comparée du cerveau. Paris: Doin et Cie. Pp. 359.

ARIENS KAPPERS, C. U. 1929. The fissures on the frontal lobes of Pithecanthropus erectus Dubois compared with those of Neanderthal man, homo recens, and chimpanzee. Proc. Kon. Akad. Wet. (Amsterdam), 32:182–95.

ASHTON, E. H. 1950. The endocranial capacities of the Australopithecinae. Proc. Zool. Soc. London, 120:715.

———. 1951. Some cranial indices of Plesianthropus and other primates. Amer. J. Phys. Anthrop., N. S. 9:283–96.

ASHTON, E. H., and ZUCKERMAN, S. 1952. Age changes in the position of the occipital condyles in the chimpanzee and gorilla. Amer. J. Phys. Anthrop., 10:277–88.

———. 1956. Age changes in the position of the foramen magnum in hominids. Proc. Zool. Soc. London, 126:313–25.

BAILEY, P., and VON BONIN, G. 1950. The Isocortex of Man. Urbana, Ill.: Univ. of Illinois Press. Pp. 300.

BAILEY, P., VON BONIN, G., and McCULLOCH, W. S. 1950. The Isocortex of the Chimpanzee. Urbana, Ill.: Univ. of Illinois Press. Pp. 440.

BECCARI, N. 1922. I centri tegmentali del rombencefalo. Riv. Pat. Nerv. Ment., 27:1.

———. 1930. I centri tegmentali dell'asse cerebrale dei Selaci. Arch. Zool. Ital., 14:411.

BERCKHEMER, F. 1937. Bemerkungen zu H. Weinerts Abhandlung "Der Urmenschenschädel von Steinheim." Verh. Ges. Phys. Anthrop., 2:49–58.

———. 1938. Vorweisung des Steinheimer Schädels im Original. Verh. Deutsch. Ges. Rassenforschg., 9:190–92.

BERNHARD, C. G., BOHM, E., and PETERSON, I. 1953. New investigations on the pyramidal system of Macaca mulatta. Experientia, 9:111–12.

BLACK, D. 1927. Lower molar hominid tooth from Choukoutien deposit. Palaeontol. Sinica, **2**:13.

BONIN, G. VON. 1934. On the size of man's brain, as indicated by skull capacity. J. Comp. Neurol., **59**:1–28.

BOULE, M., and ANTHONY, R. 1911. L'encéphale de l'homme fossile de la Chapelle-aux-Saints. L'Anthropologie, **22**:129–96.

BOWSHER, D. 1961. The termination of secondary somatosensory neurons within the thalamus of Macaca mulatta. J. Comp. Neurol., **117**: 213–27.

BRAIN, C. K. 1958. The Transvaal ape-man deposits. (Transvaal Museum Mem. 11.) Pretoria.

BRAUS, H. 1960. Lehrbuch der Anatomie des Menschen, Vol. **1**. 3d ed. Heidelberg: J. Springer.

BREUIL, ABBÉ H. 1939. Bone and antler industry of the Choukoutien Sinanthropus site. Palaeontol. Sinica, Ser. D, No. 6.

BROCA, P. 1868. Sur les crânes et ossements des Eyzies. Bull. Soc. d'Anthrop. Paris, 2d ser. **3**:350–92.

———. 1888. Mémoires sur le cerveau de l'homme et des primates. Paris: C. Reinwald.

BRODAL, A. 1957. The reticular formation of the brain stem. Edinburgh: Oliver and Boyd.

BRODMANN, K. 1909. Vergleichende Lokalisationslehre der Grosshirnrinde. Leipzig: J. A. Barth. Pp. 324.

BROOM, R. 1952. The Swartkranz ape-man, Paranthropus crassidens. (Transvaal Museum Mem. 6.) Pretoria.

BROOM, R., ROBINSON, J. T., and SCHEPERS, G. W. H. 1950. The Sterkfontein ape-man Plesianthropus. (Transvaal Museum Mem. 4.) Pretoria.

BROOM, R., and SCHEPERS, G. W. H. 1946. The South African fossil ape-man. (Transvaal Museum Mem. 2.) Pretoria.

BUCY, P. C. 1939/41. The relationship of the temporal lobes to primate behaviour. Trans. Kan. City Acad. Med.

———. 1957. Is there a pyramidal tract? Brain, **80**:376–92.

———. 1959. The basal ganglia and skeletal muscular activity. *In:* P. BAILEY and G. SCHALTENBRAND (eds.), Introduction to Stereotaxis . . . 3 vols. Stuttgart: G. Thieme.

BUCY, P. C., and KLÜVER, H. 1955. An anatomical investigation of the temporal lobe in the monkey (Macaca mulatta). J. Comp. Neurol., **103**:151–251.

CAMPBELL, A. W. 1905. Histological studies on the localization of cerebral function. Cambridge: The University Press. Pp. 360.

CHANDLER, S. B., and DEREZINSKI, C. F. 1935. The variations of the middle meningeal artery within the middle cranial fossa. Anat. Rec., **62**:309–19.

CHAPMAN, L. F., and WOLFF, H. G. 1959. The cerebral hemispheres and the highest integrative functions in man. A.M.A. Arch. Neurol., **1**:357–424.

CLARK, W. E. LE GROS. 1955. The fossil evidence for human evolution. Chicago: Univ. of Chicago Press. Pp. 181.

———. 1958. Bones of contention. J. Roy. Anthrop. Inst., **88**:1–15.

CLARK, W. E. LE GROS, and BOGGON, R. H. 1935. The thalamic connections of the parietal and frontal lobes of the brain of the monkey. Phil. Trans. Roy. Soc. London, **224B**:313–50.

CLARK, W. E. LE GROS, COOPER, D. M. and ZUCKERMAN, S. 1936. The endocranial cast of the chimpanzee. J. Roy. Anthrop. Inst., **66**:249–68.

COGHILL, G. E. 1943. Flexion spasm and mass reflexes in relation to ontogenetic development of behavior. J. Comp. Neurol., **79**:463–86.

CONRAD, K. 1954. New problems of aphasia. Brain, **77**:491–509.

CRITCHLEY, M. 1953. The parietal lobes. London: E. Arnold and Co.

CUMMINS, H. and MIDLO, C. 1943. Fingerprints, palms, and soles. Philadelphia, Pa.: Blackstone. Pp. 309.

CUNNINGHAM, D. J. 1892. Contributions to the surface anatomy of the cerebral hemispheres. (Cunningham Mem. No. 7.) Dublin: Irish Academy.

DANILEWSKI, B. 1880. Die quantitativen Bestimmungen der grauen und weissen Substanzen im Gehirn. Ztlbltt. mediz. Wissensch., **18**:241–45.

DART, R. A. 1934. The dual structure of the neopa ilium: Its history and its significance. J. Anat., **69**:1–19.

———. 1948. The Makapansgat proto-human Australopithecus prometheus. Amer. J. Phys. Anthrop., N.S. **6**:259–84.

———. 1949. The cranial-facial fragment of Australopithecus prometheus. *Ibid.*, N.S. **7**:187–214.

———. 1949a. The predatory implemental technique of Australopithecus. *Ibid.*, N.S. **7**:1–38.

———. 1949b. Innominate fragments of Australopithecus prometheus. *Ibid.*, N.S. **7**:301–34.

———. 1956. The relationships of brain size and brain pattern to human status. S. Afr. J. Med. Sci., **21**:23–45.

———. 1957. The osteodontokeratic culture of Australopithecus prometheus. (Transvaal Museum Mem. 10.) Pretoria.

———. 1959. On the evolution of language and articulate speech. Homo, **10**:154–65.

DART, R. A., and CRAIG, DENNIS. 1959. Adventures of the missing link. New York: Harper & Bros.

DUBOIS, E. 1894. Pithecanthropus erectus, eine Übergangsform. Batavia: Landesdruckerei. Pp. 59.

———. 1922. The protoaustralian fossil man of Wadjak, Java. Proc. Kon. Akad. Wet. (Amsterdam), **23**:1013–51.

———. 1924. On the principal characters of the brain in Pithecanthropus erectus. Proc. Kon. Akad. Wet. (Amsterdam), **27**:265–78.

DU BRUL, E. L. 1958. Evolution of the speech apparatus. Springfield, Ill.: C. C Thomas. Pp. 103.

DU BRUL, E. L., and SICHER, H. 1954. The adaptive chin. Springfield, Ill.: C. C Thomas. Pp. 97.

DUSSER DE BARENNE, J. G. 1924. Experimental researches on sensory localization in the cerebral cortex of the monkey. Proc. Roy. Soc. London, **96B**:272–91.

ECONOMO, C. VON. 1930. Some new methods for studying the brains of exceptional people. J. Nerv. Ment. Dis., **72**:125–34.

EICKSTEDT, E. FRHR. VON. 1952. Menschen und Menschendarstellungen der steinzeitlichen Hohlenkunst in Frankreich und Spanien. Z. Morphol. u. Anthropol., **44**:15–50, 295–344.

FILIMONOFF, I. N. 1932. Über die Variabilität der Grosshirnrindenfelder. Mitt. II, Regio occipitalis beim erwachsenen Menschen. J. Psychol. Neurol., **44**:1–86.

FOERSTER, O. 1936. Sensible corticale Felder. *In:* O. BUMKE and O. FOERSTER, Handbuch der Neurologie, **6**:1–357. Berlin: J. Springer.

FRÉDÉRIC. 1904–5. Untersuchungen über die Sinushare der Affen, nebst Bemerkungen ueber die Augenbrauen und den Schnurrbart des Menschen. Z. Morphol. u. Anthropol., **8**:239–75.

GAUL, A. 1933. Über die Wachstumsveränderungen am Geirnschädel des Orang-utan. Z. Morphol. u. Anthropol., **31**:362–94.

GIESELER, A. 1959. Die Fossilgeschichte des Menschen. *In:* G. HEBERER (ed.), Die Evolution der Organismen. Stuttgart: G. Thieme.

GIUFFRIDA-RUGGERI, V. 1912. Über die endocranischen Furchen der A. meningea media beim Menschen. Z. Morphol. u. Anthropol., **15**:401–12.

GLEES, P., and BAILEY, R. A. 1951. Cause and relations of spino-thalamic tract in man. Acta Psychiat. Neurol. Scand. (Suppl. 74), 199–206.

GLOOR, P. 1955. Electrophysiological studies on the connections of the amygdaloid nuclei in the cat. E.E.G. Clin. Neurophysiol., **7**:223–64.

GOLDSTEIN, K. 1927. Die Lokalisation in der Grosshirnrinde. *In:* A. BETHE and G. VON BERGMANN (eds.), Handbuch der normaler und pathologischer Physiologie, **10**:600–842.

GORJANOVIĆ-KRAMBERGER, K. 1906. Der diluviale Mensch von Krapina in Kroatien. Wiesbaden: W. Kreidel. Pp. 277.

GRETHER, W. F. 1939. Color vision and color blindness in monkeys. (Comp. Psychol. Monogr., No. 15). Pp. 438.

———. 1940. Chimpanzee color vision. J. Comp. Psychol., 29:167–92.

HEBB, D. O. 1949. The organization of behavior. New York: John Wiley & Sons, Inc.

HEBERER, G. 1956. Wachstumsveränderungen der Hominoidea. In: H. HOFER, A. H. SCHULTZ, and D. STARK (eds.), Primatologia, 1:339–560. Basel: S. Karger.

HENNEBERG, B. 1914. Die Verbreitung der Sinushaare bei den Säugern und die Sinushaarreste beim Menschen. Anat. Hefte, 52. Pp. 335.

HENSCHEN, S. 1930. Lichtsinn- und Farbensinnzellen im Gehirn. Deutsch. Z. Nervenheilk., 113:146, 305.

HOWELL, F. C. 1951. The place of Neanderthal man in human evolution. Amer. J. Phys. Anthrop., N.S. 9:379–416.

———. 1960. European and North African middle pleistocene hominids. Curr. Anthrop., 1:195–232.

JONES, F. W. 1929. Man's place among the mammals. London: G. Arnold & Co. Pp. 372.

KEITH, A. 1925. The antiquity of man. 2 vols. London: Williams and Norgate.

———. 1927. In: F. A. J. TURVILLE-PETRE (ed.), Researches in Prehistoric Galilee. Br. School of Archaeolog., Jerusalem. Pp. 109.

———. 1931. New discoveries relating to the antiquity of man. New York: W. W. Norton and Co. Pp. 512.

———. 1948. A new theory of human evolution. London: Watts. Pp. 151.

KLAATSCH, H. 1910. Die Aurignac Rasse und ihre Stellung im Stammbaum der Menschheit. Z. Ethnologie, 42:513–77.

KLEIST, K. 1934. Gehirnpathologie. Leipzig: J. A. Barth. Pp. 1401.

KLÜVER, H. 1951. Functional differences between the occipital and temporal lobes. In: L. A. JEFFREYS (ed.), Cerebral mechanisms in behavior, pp. 147–82.

———. 1952. Brain mechanisms and behavior with special reference to the rhinencephalon. Lancet, 72:567–77.

KLÜVER, H., and BUCY, P. C. 1939a. A preliminary analysis of the functions of the temporal lobes in monkeys. Trans. Amer. Neurol. Ass., 1939, pp. 170–75.

———. 1939b. Preliminary analysis of functions of the temporal lobes in monkeys. Arch. Neurol. Psychiat., 42:979–1000.

KOENIGSWALD, G. H. R. VON. 1938. Ein neuer Pithecanthropus Schaedel. Proc. Kon. Akad. Wet. (Amsterdam), 41:185–92.

KOENIGSWALD, G. H. R. VON. 1953. The Australopithecines and Pithecanthropus. Proc. Kon. Akad. Wet. (Amsterdam), Sec. B, 56.

KOENIGSWALD, G. H. R. VON, and WEIDENREICH, F. 1939. The relationship between Pithecanthropus and Sinanthropus. Nature, **144**:926.

KREHT, H. 1936. Zytoarchitektorik und motorisches Sprachzentrum. Z. Mikroskopischanat. Forsch., **39**:331–54.

KRUGER, L., and BERKOWITZ, E. C. 1960. The main afferent connections of the reptilian telencephalon. J. Comp. Neurol. **115**:125–41.

KURTIN, B. 1957. Mammalian migration . . . . J. Paleontol., **31**:215–27.

LAMING, A. 1959. Lascaux. Harmondsworth: Penguin Books. Pp. 208.

LASHLEY, K. S. 1929. Brain mechanisms and intelligence. Chicago: Univ. of Chicago Press. Pp. 186.

——. 1940. Persistent problems in the evolution of mind. Quart. Rev. Biol., **24**:28–42.

——. 1948. The mechanism of vision. XVIII effects of destroying the visual association areas of the monkey. Genet. Psychol. Monogr., **37**:107.

LASSEK, A. M. 1954. The pyramidal tract: Its status in medicine. Springfield, Ill.: C. C Thomas.

——. 1957. The human brain. Springfield, Ill.: C. C Thomas. Pp. 242.

LETTVIN, J. Y., MATURANA, H. R., MCCULLOCH, W. S., and PITTS, W. H. 1959. What the frog's eye tells the frog's brain. Proc. Inst. Rad. Engrs., **47**:1940–51.

LORENTE DE NÓ, R. 1957. Cerebral cortex, Architecture. *In:* J. F. FULTON (ed.), Physiology of the nervous system, pp. 274–301. 3d ed. rev. (1949). London: Oxford University Press.

MARSHALL, W. H., WOOLSEY, C. N., and BARD, P. 1945. Observations on cortical somatic mechanisms of cat and monkey. J. Neurophysiol., **14**:1–24.

MASSION, J. 1961. Contribution à l'étude de la régulation cerebelleuse du système extrapyramidal. Paris: Masson et Cie. Pp. 206.

MATURANA, H. R., LETTVIN, J. Y., MCCULLOCH, W. S., and PITTS, W. H. 1960. Anatomy and physiology of vision in the frog. J. Gen. Physiol., **43** (Suppl. 6), 129–75.

MEHLER, W. R., FEFERMAN, M. E., and NAUTA, W. J. H. 1960. Ascending depreciation following anterolateral choroidectomy in the monkey. Brain, **83**:718–50.

MEYER, A., BECK, E. and MCLARDY, T. 1947. Prefrontal lobotomy. Brain, **70**:18–49.

MEYERS, R. 1953. The extrapyramidal system: An inquiry into the validity of the concept. Neurology, **3**:627–55.

MIDLO, C., and CUMMINS, H. 1942. Palmar and plantar dermatoglyphics in primates. (Amer. Anat. Mem., No. 20.) Pp. 195.

MILLER, G. A., GALANTER, E., and PRIBRAM, K. H. 1960. Plans and structure of behavior. New York: Henry Holt & Co. Pp. 226.

MILLER, R. A. 1947. The inguinal canal of primates. Amer. J. Anat., 80:117–42.

MONAKOW, C. VON. 1895. Experimentelle und pathologisch-anatomische Untersuchungen über die Haubenregion . . . Arch. Psychiat. Nervenkr., 27:1–128.

MORANT, G. M. 1927. Studies on Paleolithic man, I. Ann. Eugen., 2:328–81.

———. 1928. Studies on Paleolithic man, II. *Ibid.* 3:337.

———. 1930. Studies on Paleolithic man, III. *Ibid.* 4:109–204.

MOUNTCASTLE, V. B., and POWELL, T. P. S. 1959. Neural mechanisms subserving cutaneous sensibility. Bull. Johns Hopkins Hosp., 105: 201–32.

OAKLEY, V. P. 1957. Man the tool-maker. Chicago: Univ. of Chicago Press. Pp. 128.

OPPENOORTH, W. F. F. 1932. Homo soloensis. Wet. Meded. Dienst Mijnbouw Nederl.-Indie, 20:46.

PACKER, A. D. 1949. A comparison of endocrania: Cast and brain of an Australian aborigine. J. Anat., 83:195–204.

PATTE, E. 1955. Les Néanderthaliens. Paris: Masson et Cie. Pp. 559.

PEARSON, K. 1925. On our present knowledge of the relationship of mind and body. Ann. Eugen., 1:382–406.

PEDEN, J. K., and BONIN, G. v. 1947. The Neocortex of Hapale. J. Comp. Neurol., 86:37–64.

PENFIELD, W., and RASMUSSEN, T. 1950. The cerebral cortex of man. New York: Macmillan Co. Pp. 248.

PENFIELD, W., and ROBERTS, L. 1959. Speech and brain mechanisms. Princeton: Princeton Univ. Press.

PIVETEAU, J., and DECHASEAUX, C. 1957. Traité de Paléontologie. Vol. 7 (Vers la forme humaine . . .). Paris: Masson et Cie.

POLIAKOV, G. I. 1961. Some results of research into the development of the neural structure of the cortical ends of analyzers in man. J. Comp. Neurol., 117:197–212.

POLYAK, S. 1957. The vertebrate visual system, ed. H. KLÜVER. Chicago: Univ. of Chicago Press. Pp. 1390.

POOL, L. 1949. Selective partial ablation of the frontal cortex. New York: Harper & Bros.

POWELL, T. P. S., and MOUNTCASTLE, V. B. 1959. Some aspects of the functional organization of the cortex of the postcentral gyrus of the monkey. Bull. Johns Hopkins Hosp., 105:132–62.

ROBINSON, J. T. 1953. Meganthropus, Australopithecines and hominids. Amer. J. Phys. Anthrop., N.S. 11:1–38.

ROBINSON, J. T. 1955. Further remarks on the relationship between Meganthropus and Australopithecines. *Ibid.*, N.S. **13**:429–46.

——. 1956. The dentition of the Australopithecines. (Transvaal Museum Mem. 9.) Pretoria.

——. 1961. The Australopithecines and their bearing on the origin of man and of stone tool making. S. Afr. J. Sci., **57**:3–11.

ROTHMAN, D. 1937. The endocranial course of the middle meningeal artery in American whites and Negroes. Amer. J. Phys. Anthrop., **22**:425–35.

SCHEIBEL, M. E., and SCHEIBEL, A. B. 1958. Structural substrates for integrative patterns in the brain stem reticular core. *In:* HERBERT H. JASPER *et al.* (eds.), Reticular formation of the brain, pp. 31–55. Boston: Little, Brown & Co.

SCHUELL, H. 1960. Clinical findings in aphasia. Lancet, **80**:482–90.

SCHULTZ, A. H. 1926. Fetal growth of man and other primates. Quart. Rev. Biol., **1**:465–521.

——. 1930. The skeleton of the trunk and the limbs in higher primates. Hum. Biol., **2**:303–438.

——. 1940*a*. The size of the orbit and the eye in primates. Amer. J. Phys. Anthrop., **26**:489–508.

——. 1940*b*. Growth and development of the chimpanzee. (Contributions to Embryology, Carnegie Inst., No. 28, pp. 1–63.)

——. 1941. Growth and development of the orang-utan. (Contributions to Embryology, Carnegie Inst., No. 29, pp. 57–110.)

——. 1944. Age changes and variability in gibbons. Amer. J. Phys. Anthrop., N.S. **12**:145–80.

——. 1945. The number of vertebra in primates. Proc. Amer. Philos. Soc., **89**:601–26.

——. 1947. Variability in man and other primates. Amer. J. Phys. Anthrop., N.S. **5**:1–14.

——. 1949. Sex differences in the pelves of primates. *Ibid.*, N.S. **7**:401–24.

——. 1950. The physical distinctions of man. Proc. Amer. Philos. Soc., **94**:428–49.

——. 1955. The position of the occipital condyles and of the face relative to the skull base in primates. Amer. J. Phys. Anthrop., N.S. **13**:97–120.

SCHWALBE, G. 1899. Studien über Pithecanthropus erectus. Z. Morphol. u. Anthropol., **1**:1–240.

SINGER, R. 1954. The Saldanha skull from Hopefield, South Africa. Amer. J. Phys. Anthrop., N.S. **12**:345–62.

——. 1957. Investigations at the Hopefield site. *In:* J. DESMOND CLARK (ed.), Proceedings of the 3d Pan-African Congress on Prehistory (1955), pp. 175–82. London: Chatto & Windus.

SLIJPER, E. J. 1946. Comparative biologic-anatomical investigations on the vertebral column and spinal musculature in mammals. Nederl. Akad. Wet. Verh., 2d Ser., Part 42, No. 5. Pp. 122.

SMITH, G. ELLIOT. 1928. Endocranial cast obtained from Rhodesian skull. *In:* Rhodesian man and associated remains. London: British Museum, Nos. 53–58.

STRAUS, W. L., JR. 1929. Studies on the primate ilia. Amer. J. Anat., **43**:403–60.

———. 1949. The riddle of man's ancestry. Quart. Rev. Biol., **24**:200–233.

———. 1961. Review of E. Lloyd Du Brul's Evolution of the speech apparatus. Amer. J. Phys. Anthrop., N.S. **18**:324–25.

STREET, B. 1957. Hearing loss in aphasia. J. Speech Hearing Dis., **22**:60–67.

SWANSCOMBE COMMITTEE. 1938. Report on the Swanscombe skull. J. Roy. Anthrop. Inst., **68**:17–98.

SYMINGTON, J. 1916. Endocranial casts and the brain form: A criticism of some recent speculations. J. Anat. (London), **53** (1915–16): 130.

TESTUT, L. 1889. Recherches anthropologie sur le squelette quatervaire de chancelade. Bull. Soc. d'Anthropol. de Lyon, **8**:131–253.

TILDESLEY, M. L., and DATTA-MAJUNDER, N. 1944. Cranial capacity data. Amer. J. Phys. Anthrop., N.S. **2**:233–50.

TODD, WINGATE T. 1927. A liter and a half of brain. Science, **66**:122–25.

TRETJAKOFF, D. 1910. Die Nervenendigungen an den Sinushaaren des Rindes. Z. Wiss. Zool., **97**:314–416.

VALLOIS, H. V. La capacité cranienne chez les primates superieurs et le "rubicon cérébral." C. R. Acad. Sci., **238**:1349–51.

VERNEAU, R. 1906–19. Les Grottes de Grimaldi. 2 vols. Monaco: Imp. de Monaco.

VERWORN, M., R. BONNETT, R., and STEINMANN, A. 1919. Der diluviale Menschenfund von Obercassel bei Bonn. Wiesbaden: S. F. Bergmann. Pp. 193.

VOGT, O., and VOGT, C. 1919. Allgemeine Ergebnisse unserer Hirnforschung. J. Psychol. Neurol., **25**:279–461.

WALKER, A. E. 1938. The primate thalamus. Chicago: Univ. of Chicago Press. Pp. 321.

WATERMAN, H. C. 1929. Studies on the evolution of the pelvis of man and other primates. Bull. Amer. Mus. Nat. Hist., **58**:585–642.

WEIDENREICH, F. 1928. Der Schädelfund von Weimar-Ehringsdorf. Jena: Fischer.

———. 1936. Observations on the form and proportions of the endocranial casts of Sinanthropus pekinensis. Palaeont. Sinica, Ser. D, No. 7. Pp. 450.

WEIDENREICH, F. 1938. The ramification of the middle meningeal artery in fossil hominids and its bearing upon phylogenetic problems. Palaeontol. Sinica, Ser. D, No. 3, Pp. 16.

——. 1941. The brain and its role in the phylogenetic transformation of the human skull. Trans. Amer. Philos. Soc., N.S. 31:321–442.

——. 1943. The skull of Sinanthropus pekinensis. Palaeont. Sinica., Ser. D, No. 10.

——. 1947. Some particulars of skull and brain of early hominids. Amer. J. Phys. Anthropol., N.S. 5:357–427.

——. 1951. Morphology of Solo man. Am. Mus. of Nat. Hist. (Anthropol. Pap. 43), 3:205–90.

WEINERT, H. 1928. Pithecanthropus erectus. Z. Anat., 87:429–547.

——. 1936. Steinheim skull.

——. 1956. Der Urmenschenschädel von Steinheim. Z. Morphol. u. Anthropol., 35:483–516.

WEIZSÄCKER, V. VON. 1947. Der Gestaltkreis. 3d ed. Stuttgart: G. Thieme. Pp. 208.

WOOLSEY, C. N. 1958. Organization of sensory and motor areas. *In:* H. F. HARLOW and C. N. WOOLSEY (eds.), Biological and biochemical bases of behavior, pp. 63–81. Madison: Univ. of Wisconsin Press.

WOOLSEY, C. N., and CHANG, H. T. 1948. Activation of the cerebral cortex by antidromic volleys in the pyramidal tract. Proc. Ass. Res. Nerv. Ment. Dis., 27:146, 161.

ZUCKERMAN, S. 1953. Correlation of change in the evolution of higher primates. *In:* A. C. HARDY and E. B. FORD (eds.), Evolution as a process, pp. 300–52. London: Allen & Unwin.

# Index

# Index

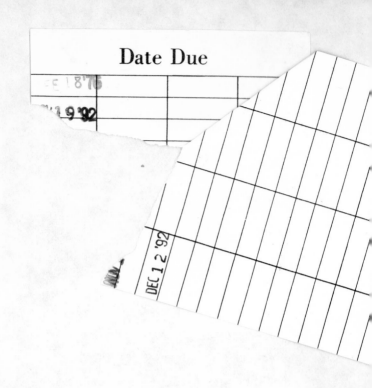